> **"Can you imagine silver leaves waving above a pool of liquid gold containing singing fishes? Twin suns that circle and fall in a rainbow heaven, another world in the sky? If you come with me, I'll show you all this – and it will be, I promise you, the dullest part of it all. . ."**
>
> *Speech by the First Doctor,*
> *(Accredited to the series' first story editor,*
> *David Whitaker)*

Flyleaf Illustration by **Alister Pearson**
Brief Encounters illustrated by
Paul Vyse

Co-ordinator: **John Freeman**
Spatial Designer: **Gary Gilbert**
Assistant TARDIS Engineers:
Dan Abnett, Jacqui Papp
Additional Dimension Checks:
Andrew Pixley
Segonax Promotion Controller:
Jane Sumner
Gallifreyan Production Engineer:
Julie Speller
Adviser: **John Nathan-Turner**

Feature Writers: Stephen James Walker, Gary Russell, John Nathan-Turner and Sophie Aldred.

Episode Guide compiled by **Paul Travers** and **Andrew Pixley**. 'Firsts' by Andrew Pixley. With thanks to all contributors, Jeremy Bentham, David Howe, Adam Lee at BBC Archives, BBC Video, Target Books, Barry Newbery, Raymond P. Cusick and Tomek Bork.

Where it all began

Stephen James Walker delves into *Doctor Who*'s earliest origins.

As is now common knowledge, the original inspiration for *Doctor Who* came from Canadian producer Sydney Newman shortly after he joined the BBC as Head of Drama in December 1962. However, the full story of how the series was developed from there into the form in which it eventually reached the nation's screens is much less well-known.

The need for a new series arose in the first place simply because the BBC's programme planners decided that there was a gap to be filled in their Saturday evening schedule between the end of the sports coverage at 5:15 and the start of the pop music show *Juke Box Jury* at 5:45. This slot had previously been occupied by children's classic drama serials, but these rarely won high ratings and the idea was to move them to Sunday afternoons if Drama could come up with something more suitable.

What Sydney Newman was after, therefore, was a series which would appeal equally to sports fans and to the young pop music audience – to bridge the gap between the two shows either side – and which would also attract children accustomed to their teatime serials. Inspired partly by HG Wells' *The Time Machine* he hit upon the idea of a time travel adventure exploring scientific and historical themes which could be described as educational, or at least mind-opening, for children watching. Although space travel would obviously come into it, he was keen that the series should avoid 'bug-eyed monsters', which he saw as the lowest form of science-fiction.

For the time machine itself, Newman came up with the concept of a ship larger inside than out, which he thought should be disguised as an everyday object so that viewers would be encouraged not to take things for granted. To answer the questions of how the ship came to be on Earth and who owned it he then devised the character of a crotchety old man, senile but with extraordinary flashes of brilliance, who had escaped in terror from an advanced civilisation on a far-distant planet. This old man would not be fully in control of the ship, however, so his attempts to return his human ➤

5

"DOCTOR WHO"
THE ORIGINAL GUIDE

General notes on Background and Approach for an exciting adventure – Science Fiction Drama serial for Childrens Saturday viewing.

The serial will run for 52 weeks and will be a series of stories, each in themselves separate entities but linked to make up the continuity. Each story will run from between 4 to 10 episodes and each episode will have its own title and be of 30 minutes in length. Every episode will reach a climax about halfway through and end with a strong cliff hanger.

APPROACH TO THE STORIES

The series is neither fantasy nor space travel nor science fiction. The basic premise is that four characters are projected into real environments based on the best factual information of situations in time and space and in any material state we can realise in practical terms.

Using unusual, exciting backgrounds or ordinary backgrounds seen unusually, each story will have a strong informational core based on fact. Our central characters, because of their 'ship' may find themselves on the shores of Britain when Caesar and his legionnaires landed in 44 B.C., may find themselves in their own school laboratories but reduced to the size of a pinhead; or on the dying planet Mars or some as yet undiscovered world in another galaxy which seems identical to Earth yet where certain values are altered, laughter being the worst possible insult and sneezing a criminal offence.

The series, by the use of the characters in action stories, is designed to bridge the gap between our massive audience who watch sport on Saturday afternoon and those teenagers who watch Juke Box Jury.

It is emphasised that the 'ship' may transport the four characters backwards or forwards, sideways into lesser or greater dimenions or into non-gravitational existence or invisibility etcetera but once arrived into the different place and time the four characters have only their intelligence and ingenuity upon which to rely. They cannot produce a 'ray gun' to reduce a horde of Picts and Scots nor can they rely upon specialised drugs to cure a Greek philosopher.

It is also emphasised that the four characters cannot make history. Advice must not be proferred to

6

Although the series creator Sydney Newman was adamant *Doctor Who* was not to feature Bug Eyed Monsters, the Daleks' success marked a change in original intent, despite touching on contemporary issues of the day such as the fear of nuclear war. Photo © Raymond P. Cusick.

companions home would always lead them into new adventures in space and time.

Sometime early in 1963, Newman put all thse ideas into a short memo which he gave to the Head of the Script Department, Donald Wilson. Although a little sceptical at first, Wilson agreed to take the memo away and have some further work done. Progress was not as smooth as it might have been, though, owing to the fact that the whole Drama Group was in a state of some upheaval at that time following the introduction by Newman of some important organisational changes.

One of these changes was the splitting up of Drama into three separate Departments – Series, Serials and Plays – each with its own Head who would exercise direct control and be answerable to Newman. Another was the establishment of the 'production team' system and consequent abolition of the Script Department. (Previously, every producer had been his own director – the two terms had been

interchangeable – and the Script Department had existed to find writers for particular productions.) Naturally, these changes did not take place overnight and the embryonic *Doctor Who* was caught up in them. Donald Wilson himself was transferring from the Script Department to become Head of the new Serials Department during this period; and one of the first people with whom Sydney Newman discussed his ideas for *Doctor Who* was in fact an old-style producer/director, Rex Tucker (who was later to direct *The Gunfighters).*

AN UNDERESTIMATED ROLE

Tucker's contribution to the development of *Doctor Who* has long been understimated. Although never formally appointed or credited as such he was, in effect, the series' first producer. His role, as he saw it, was very much a temporary one, to get things started on the right track

The Doctor examines soil samples at the end of *The Daleks,* watched by the victorious Thals. Photo © Raymond P. Cusick.

Confrontation: Ian Chesterton (William Russell) and Marco Polo (Mark Eden) clash with Susan (Carole Ann Ford) and the Doctor (William Hartnell) during the story *Marco Polo*. Photo © Barry Newbery.

pending the arrival of Sydney Newman's chosen producer, Verity Lambert. However, he was certainly more than just a 'caretaker'. For one thing, it may well have been he who came up with the title *Doctor Who* (although he personally denies this, giving the credit to Sydney Newman). Undoubtedly he helped to develop Newman's original idea and the basic dramatic structure of the series. In addition, he was initially responsible for setting up the technical side of the production and for taking decisions on the scripting.

At this stage, however, scripting itself was still the responsibility of the Script Department, and the man asked to handle the new project was C.E. Webber (known to all at the BBC as 'Bunny'), another man whose contribution to *Doctor Who* has long been misunderstood. Webber's task was in fact two-fold: first, he had to flesh out the basic idea handed down to him and produce a more detailed format for the series; secondly, he had to write the scripts for the episodes intended to comprise the first televised story. By this stage, Sydney Newman had ceased to have any day-to-day involvement with the series, and although Webber would certainly have discussed his ideas quite extensively with Donald Wilson (and probably also with Rex Tucker) it is

clear that he himself devised a number of important elements of *Doctor Who*.

In particular, it was Webber who thought up the actual characters of the two teachers, Ian and Barbara, and decided that the young girl in the story, Susan, should be a pupil at their school – although, admittedly, the way he envisaged these characters was not quite how they turned out. Originally, Ian and Barbara were to have been somewhat younger than they eventually appeared. Susan, on the other hand, was intended to be a cross between Andromeda, the other-worldly character from *A for Andromeda* and *The Andromeda Breakthrough* (two BBC science fiction serials from 1961 and 1962 respectively) and Honor Blackman's karate-kicking *Avengers* girl. Apparently, Webber even had some casting ideas, thinking that Ian could be played by pop star Cliff Richard and one of the girls – presumably Barbara – by Susan Hampshire!

In Webber's original script the Doctor was to have taken the other three characters on a journey in his time-space machine and landed them in an adventure where they were all reduced to just an inch in height (an idea probably contained in Sydney Newman's original memo and later re-used in the transmitted story *Planet of Giants*). However, ➤

Nelson on his battle tactics when approaching the Nile nor must bon mots be put into the mouth of Oscar Wilde. They are four people plunged into alien surroundings armed with only their courage and cleverness.

CHARACTERS:
DOCTOR WHO

A name given to him by his two unwilling fellow travellers, Barbara Wright and Ian Chesterton, simply because they don't know who he is and he is happy to extend the mystery surrounding him. They do know that he is a Doctor of Science and that he is over sixty. He is frail looking but wiry and tough like an old turkey and this latter is amply demonstrated whenever he is forced to run away from danger. His watery blue eyes, are continually looking around in bewilderment and occasionally suspicion clouds his face when he assumes his decisions are being opposed by his earthly 'passengers'. He can be enormously cunning once he feels he is being conspired against and he sometimes acts with impulse more than reasoned intelligence. He can be quite considerate and wise and he responds to intelligence eagerly. His forgetfulness and vagueness alternate with flashes of brilliant thought and deduction. He has escaped from the 50th century because he has found life at that time to be unpleasant and he is searching for another existence into which he can settle. Insofar as his operation of the 'ship' is concerned he is much like the average driver of a motor car in that he is its master when it works properly and its bewildered slave when it is temperamental. Because he is somewhat pathetic, his grand-daughter and the other two continually try to help him find 'home' but they are never sure of his motives.

SUSAN

The Doctor's grand-daughter, aged fifteen. She is a sharp intelligent girl,

Susan (Carole Ann Ford) in *The Keys of Marinus*. Photo © Raymond P. Cusick.

quick and perky. She makes mistakes, however, because of inexperience. Addicted to 20th Century contemporary slang and likes pop records – in fact, she admires the life teenagers enjoy in 1963. At the beginning of the story, she has persuaded her Grandfather to stay in 1963 so that she can go to school and create at least one complete section of experience. Since she has been visiting all sorts of existences and places with her Grandfather, Susan has a wide general knowledge and on some subjects can be brilliantly factual. On other matters, she is lamentably ignorant. She has something of a crush on Ian Chesterton.

Ian Chesterton (William Russell) in *Marco Polo*. Photo © BBC.

IAN CHESTERTON

27, red-brick University type, a teacher of applied science at Susan's school. A good physical specimen, a gymnast, dexterous with his hands and fortunate to possess the patience to deal with Doctor Who and his irrational moods. He occasionally clashes with the Doctor on decisions but for all the Doctor's superior scientific knowledge, is able to make intelligent enquiry and bring sound common sense to bear at moments of stress.

8

as things turned out, Rex Tucker decided to reject Webber's script. Although very much part of the 'old guard' himself, he realised that what his friend had written was too cerebral and constituted the sort of old-fashioned children's drama that Sydney Newman was anxious to get away from.

In the meantime, Tucker had been having his own ideas about casting. He had found a young Australian actress (whose name he no longer recalls) for the part of Susan and approached his friend Hugh David (later to direct *Fury From The Deep* but at that time working as an actor) to play the central role of the Doctor; an offer which David declined. Other aspects of the production to which Tucker turned his attention included even the music, inviting composer Tristram Cary to write the signature tune and the incidentals for the first story. Around April 1963, however, Tucker's stint on the embryonic series came to an end as he left to take a holiday abroad, bringing to a close a period which can be seen, in retrospect, as something of a 'false start' for *Doctor Who).*

Following the rejection of Bunny Webber's script, Donald Wilson had asked another in-house writer, Australian Anthony Coburn, to try his hand at writing a suitable opening story, working from the existing format. At about the same time, Wilson had also appointed David Whitaker, again an established BBC staffer, to be the series' first script editor under the new production team regime.

FIRST DRAFTS

By the end of April 1963 Coburn had delivered his first draft scripts and he and Whitaker had begun to discuss them. It was also at around this time that another key development occurred: the arrival of Verity Lambert as producer. Lambert had previously been Sydney Newman's production secretary on the *Armchair Theatre* plays he had produced for ABC TV and she was just the sort of sharp, young, forward-looking person he wanted in charge of *Doctor Who*. Like him, she was keen that it should be a radical departure from anything the BBC had done before, and she very quickly demonstrated this by negating all Rex Tucker's earlier decisions. Tucker himself was by no means disappointed about this – he wasn't keen on *Doctor Who* and wanted to move on to other things – but Donald Wilson still thought there should be someone senior and experienced working on the series as an advisor. Consequently, after Tucker's departure, Wilson persuaded Sydney Newman to agree to the appointment of an Associate Producer, namely Mervyn Pinfield.

The first episode of Anthony Coburn's four part opening story was partly based on Bunny Webber's rejected draft but the other three, set in the stone age, were completely new. Whitaker requested a number of rewrites, basically to tone down the 'educational' content and make the story more exciting, but he was happy enough with what he had seen to ask Coburn also to produce a storyline for the second serial, intended to be a six-parter. He also readily accepted Coburn's suggestions that the Doctor's ship should be disguised as a police box and called TARDIS, and that Susan should be his grand-daughter rather than just a young travelling companion.

During May and June 1963, having rejected Rex Tucker's

The mix of regular characters was carefully considered before the series began. Ian, Barbara and the Doctor in discussion in *The Keys of Marinus*. Photo © Raymond P. Cusick.

choices, Verity Lambert set about assembling her own regular cast for the series, eventually selecting the now-familiar team of William Hartnell, William Russell, Jacqueline Hill and Carole Ann Ford. David Whitaker, meanwhile, turned his mind to commissioning more scripts, and as a first step he prepared a full Writers' Guide to the series. This was drawn primarily from Bunny Webber's original format but the character outlines were modified somewhat to reflect the changes Whitaker had agreed with Anthony Coburn.

The entire contents of the Writers' Guide are reprinted alongside this article and, as can be seen, it represents a fascinating 'snapshot' of the series mid-way between its original conception and its final televised form. It also shows that directors had now been assigned to

Ian and Barbara find themselves captives in Morphoton during *The Keys of Marinus*. Photo © Raymond P. Cusick.

the show, with the responsibility of handling the first story falling to Waris Hussein. Rex Tucker, meanwhile, was scheduled to take on the second story (although, curiously, he now denies having had any knowledge of this, maintaining that he would never have agreed to it).

Although the Writers' Guide contained short synopses of Anthony Coburn's two stories – now bearing the titles *Dr Who and the Tribe of Gum* and *Dr Who and the Robots* – work on these scripts was actually progressing far from smoothly. Even though Coburn had carried out the requested re-writes on *The Tribe of Gum*, Whitaker and Lambert remained unhappy with it. In the end, however, they decided to persevere, mainly because they didn't have time to commission a substitute. Another small hiccup occurred at the end of June 1963,

though, when the demise of the Script Department virtually forced Coburn to go freelance and Whitaker had formally to commission him to continue working on his scripts.

NO BUG-EYED MONSTERS

By this time, Whitaker had sent copies of the Writers' Guide to a number of other freelance writers (and writers' agents) – mainly friends or friends of friends – and storylines soon started arriving on his desk. The first new writer to be commissioned, in mid-July 1963, was Canadian John Lucarotti whose story, at that time titled *Dr Who and a Journey to Cathay,* involved the Doctor and his friends meeting Marco Polo. Next, at the end of July, Terry Nation was commissioned to

write a six-parter about a race of creatures called Daleks, based on a storyline he had submitted entitled *The Survivors.*

As August and September 1963 went by and further impressive storylines came in, David Whitaker began to assemble the package of stories that would make up the fifty-two week series. John Lucarotti and Terry Nation each had a second serial commissioned while Dennis Spooner, a good friend of Nation's, was asked to contribute a historical segment. Storylines by other writers were also under consideration. However, when, in mid-September, Anthony Coburn delivered his first drafts for *The Robots,* now retitled *The Masters of Luxor,* the production team were dissatisfied with them and decided to drop the story in favour of Terry Nation's Dalek serial (now expanded to seven ➤

Barbara Wright (Jacqueline Hill) in trouble in *The Aztecs.* Photo © Barry Newbery.

BARBARA WRIGHT
23, attractive. A History teacher at the same school. Timid but capable of sudden courage. Although there is no question of a developing love story between her and Ian, her admiration for him results in undercurrents of antagonism between her and Susan.

The Ship:
Doctor Who has a 'ship' which can travel through space, through time and through matter. It is a product of the year 5733 and cannot travel forward from that date (otherwise the Doctor and Sue could discover their own destinies) the authorities of the 50th Century deeming forward sight unlawful. This still enables Ian and Barbara (and the audience) to see into environments and existencies far beyond the present day. The Ship, when first seen, has the outward appearance of a police box, but the inside reveals an extensive electronic contrivance and comfortable living quarters with occasional bric-a-brac acquired by the Doctor in his travels. Primarily, the machine has a yearo-

9

meter, which allows the traveller to select his stopping place. In the first story, however, the controls are damaged and the 'ship' becomes uncertain in performance, which explains why Ian and Barbara, once set upon their journey, are never able to return to their own time and place in their natural forms.

THE FIRST STORY of four episodes, written by Anthony Coburn begins the journey and takes the four travellers back in time to 100,000 B.C. to mid-paleolithic man and it is in this story that the 'ship' is slightly damaged and forever afterwards is erratic in certain sections of its controls.

THE SECOND STORY of six episodes, written by Anthony Coburn takes the travellers to some time approximately near the 30th Century, forward to the world when it is inhabited only by robots, where humanity has died away. The robots themselves, used to a life of service, have invented a master robot capable of original thought but realising the dangers have rendered their invention inoperative, even though it means they must sink into total inertia. The travellers, unaware of this situation, bring the robots and then the new invention 'to life', and face the dangers inherent in a pitiless computer.

Since this is primarily a series of stories concerning people rather than studio effects, and the original characters and backgrounds have been prepared already, the writer will be asked to submit a story line from which he will be commissioned. This need not go into fractional detail – three or four pages of quarto ought to be sufficient to express the idea.

Technical advice is available insofar as what may or may not be achieveed in the studio but every endeavour will be made to meet the requirements of your story. There is a certain film budget, not extensive but sufficient to cover most contingencies and the episodes will be ampexed so that a 'stop and start' may be achieved if desired.

Writers may consult the story editor who will work out their plots and situations with them and arrange meetings with the Associate Producer who acts as the arbiter on technical and factual detail.

Characters and backgrounds prepared for the BBC by: Donald Wilson, C.E. Webber, Sydney Newman.
Producer: Verity Lambert.
Assoc. Producer: Mervyn Pinfield.
Story Editor: David Whitaker.
Directors: Waris Hussein, Rex Tucker.

◄ episodes and retitled *The Mutants*).

In the meantime, though, Coburn's other story, now given its final title of *100,000 BC*, was gradually progressing towards recording – despite the fact that the production team were working against a background of some hostility from others in the BBC who resented Sydney Newman's 'new broom' approach. Even Sydney Newman and Donald Wilson had their doubts when they were shown the scripts for *The Mutants,* feeling that the story constituted precisely the sort of 'bug-eyed monster' science fiction that they did not want to see in the series. In the end, the only thing that saved this now-legendary story was that, as with *100,000 BC,* there simply wasn't time to commission a replacement! Another problem arose when it was realised that the sets for John Lucarotti's *Marco Polo* and Terry Nation's *The Keys of Marinus* could not be got ready in time, but this was solved by David Whitaker hastily writing a two part story himself, set entirely within the TARDIS (*Inside the Spaceship,* often referred to incorrectly as *The Edge of Destruction*).

Of course, despite all these problems, *Doctor Who* did go into production as planned and indeed on schedule. The first filming took place on 20th August 1963 with the shooting of the innovative title sequence designed by Bernard Lodge (based on the 'howl-around' effect earlier devised by Mervyn Pinfield). Subsequently the unique

theme music was written by composer Ron Grainer and realised by Delia Derbyshire and assistant Dick Mills at the Radiophonic Workshop. Then, on Friday 13th September, there took place an 'experimental session' in the recording studio, the aim of which was simply to get the sets erected for a 'trial run', to iron out any technical problems which might occur on this unusually complex show.

Filming for the series' first episode took place at the BBC's Ealing Studios on 19th September 1963 and the episode itself was recorded in Studio D, Lime Grove, just eight days later on Friday 27th September. The intention was that if this recording proved successful it would be transmitted as the series' opening episode on Saturday 16th November; if not, it would be re-recorded on Friday 18th October and transmission would begin on 23rd November. As things transpired, Sydney Newman and Donald Wilson requested a number of changes to dialogue and character-isation and a general tightening up of the direction after seeing the pilot, so events followed the latter of these two courses.

Despite the furore surrounding President Kennedy's assassination the previous day, the first episode of *Doctor Who* was eventually broadcast only slightly later than scheduled, at sixteen minutes and twenty seconds after five o'clock on Saturday 23rd November 1963. A legend had begun.

The Meeting

I live in France and often visit Paris where one of my favourite haunts is a small inn called *L'Auberge du Pont Romain* on the Ile de Cité. There is nothing remarkable about the auberge, there must be hundreds almost identical to it around. Almost but not quite. For despite its expresso coffee-making and all the other accoutrements of our day and age the auberge has an atmosphere which I find unique. It reeks of history. Perhaps it is the oak beams or the old fireplace which gives me this feeling of timelessness, even though the mantlepiece is laden with pennants, trophies and photographs of a leading Parisian football club.

Anyway, about the middle of last October I popped in for a glass of Medoc, one of my favourite wines, and was just about to order it when a voice behind me said, "Ah, Lucarotti, you'll take this one with me, I trust." The voice was unmistakeable and when I turned to face the Doctor he smiled at me.

"Remember all this?," he asked with a gesture at our surroundings. "Fifteen ninety-something and those two young bloods, Gaston de-Whatsisname and that other one, the Huguenot fellow." I remembered all too well. Gaston was the Huguenot, Simon Duval, the Catholic. but I knew better than to correct him. "So what'll it be?" he asked. "A M-Medoc", I stammered. "Deux Medocs," he said to the waiter as we sat at a table.

"What are you doing here?" I blurted.

"Visiting you," he replied.

"But the Time Lords retired you ages ago." The waiter served our wine and the Doctor clinked my glass with his.

"Mustn't lose touch with old friends," he replied with a wink and sipped his wine. I took a big swig of mine.

"No, no. This is impossible," I pointed at his face and wagged my fore-finger. "You are a figment of my imagination."

As, no doubt, is the place we're sitting in now", the Doctor observed dryly, raising his glass to the light to study the colour of the wine. "Fifteen ninety-seven was a terribly good year as well. Marvellous bouquet."

"I wouldn't know. I wasn't around". I felt crushed.

"Shame," the Doctor shrugged and then asked brightly "Not thinking of going to Samarkand, are you?"

"No," I was bemused. "Should I be?"

"Well, I can always sneak out of you-know-where and come to where-you-are as long as we've both been there together. You can get me there you see. D'you understand?"

"Let me work on it," I closed my eyes momentarily and when I re-opened them the Doctor was gone. As was his glass. Obviously, for some strange reason I had temporarily freaked out. I called the waiter and asked for my bill.

"It was paid, monsieur," he replied, "by the little old man with the long grey hair who just left."

I am planning my trip to Samarkand.

John Lucarotti

The Doctor Ordered

The Three Doctors threw the first three incarnations of the time traveller into a reluctant alliance. Photo © BBC.

Gary Russell examines the *Doctor Who* legend, which is still producing new adventures today . . .

The Doctors' many companions have often reflected the decade in which they appeared. If Ben and Polly were indicative of the Swinging Sixties, so Sarah Jane became the new woman of the Seventies. If Tegan mirrored the tough young lady of the Eighties, so Ace became the streetwise, cocksure young girl of the Nineties.

But in many ways, each of the seven Doctors have also been a reflection of the fads and fashions of their day, although some far more than others. To explain this, let's go back to where it all began, when television drama started to be more challenging and also less pompous – the early Sixties.

The title of the series itself may have seemed very ambiguous to the television viewers when they tuned in on November 23rd, 1963. It may well have scuppered a lot of potential viewers before it even started! Early Sixties television was proliferated by tv drama series about the medical profession, a few made by the BBC itself but the majority imported from America, such as the famous *Doctor Kildare*. Turning to the *Radio Times*, the viewing public could well be expected to mutter, "Oh no, not another medical show!"

The Celestial Toymaker proves a deadly adversary for the First Doctor, played by Michael Gough. Photo © BBC.

To combat that possibility *Doctor Who's* very first producer, Verity Lambert, took a very radical step, making sure her leading character was not a young, dashing hero. Instead, both she and her production team – comprising Script Editor David Whitaker, Associate Producer Mervyn Pinfield and the director of the first story, Waris Hussein – and the Head of BBC Drama Sydney Newman (who also created the cult show *The Avengers* for ABC Television) started looking for someone fit and agile enough to survive a demanding series, but mature enough not to appear a dashing hero.

A CROTCHETY OLD MAN

Actors such as Leslie French and Cyril Cusak were considered before Verity settled on William Hartnell, a character actor usually associated with tough, no-nonsense roles and certainly not known to children. Many people who worked on the show during Hartnell's three years comment that he was a somewhat grumpy, unpleasant and easily irritated but thoroughly professional man who, although only in his early sixties, frequently acted as if he were nearly ninety! Others will say that he was a kindly, charming statesman-like figure, definitely a leader of his team, but always welcoming to strangers.

His characterisation of the Doctor was, however, very distinct and rarely atypical. The First Doctor was a no-nonsense, prickly man, who rarely approved of his younger companions, took very little advice from others and also believed (or pretended to believe) he knew best. Although in his first appearances he came over as somewhat alarming and perhaps a little frightening, he mellowed as the stories progressed. However, he very rarely let the facade of complete indifference slip.

The Doctor could never be seen, least of all by himself, to be too content, too relaxed or too emotional about anything. A lot of very sad things happened to him in the early days – his initial travelling companion Susan, his granddaughter, eventually discovered love and left the comfort of the TARDIS. She was followed by the two school teachers Ian and Barbara who joined the Doctor in the first televised adventure, suddenly taking the opportunity to escape home to Earth.

All three departures seemed to make the Doctor a lot less selfish and arrogant but also far more vulnerable and perhaps a little bit older. Once Ian and Barbara had left, the Doctor found himself surrounded by a variety of much younger companions, some like Vicki or Dodo barely into their teens. Although the Doctor felt equally protective towards them, there was nevertheless still a need

for him to be obtuse and frequently obnoxious, belittling or embarrassing them. Indeed the one time the Doctor truly allowed himself a fragment of self pity, as he reflected on his apparently self-imposed exile and all the people he had known who had now left him, he did it in complete isolation, for fear of displaying any weakness.

When he was joined by Dodo (who wandered into the TARDIS on Wimbledon Common!) and reunited with Steven, whose hurt and bitter desertion had initiated the melancholy, the Doctor quickly hid his pleasure at these events under his usual armour of one-upmanship and casual disinterest. However, there is no doubt that all of this displayed a totally understandable and decidedly likeable old fuddy duddy. The viewers at least knew what was going on even if his companions did not!

THE COSMIC HOBO

If the Hartnell Doctor represented the authoritarian post-war early Sixties, the second Doctor, played by the much younger looking Patrick Troughton, was a complete antithesis of his predecessor in much the same way that the latter years of the Sixties were radically different to the early ones. Indeed, radicalism personified the second Doctor. If Hartnell was every bit the overseer, then Troughton's Doctor was the ➤

The cosmic hobo, Patrick Troughton. Photo © BBC.

◄ underdog, the subversive. As Hartnell automatically took charge, so Troughton instinctively challenged any and all authority, showing it to be almost without exception flawed and ill-conceived. The Second Doctor was a literal little man against the big men, always in the middle of events, jumping up and down and telling those supposedly in charge that they were being inconsiderate and foolish.

Troughton's relationships with his travelling companions was also much more casual. He never instilled any kind of pecking order, merely a mutual respect and fondness. Although Ben and Polly remained with him for a short time, the majority of this Doctor's regeneration was spent surrounded by anachronistic companions, leaving contemporary companions behind and concentrating on people from the past or future. That way the emphasis for the audience shifted away from the companion and for the first time onto the Doctor, increasing our familiarity with him. This change didn't prevent engaging our sympathy for the companions when the Doctor had to explain how an electric train worked to Jamie, a Scot from the eighteenth century, or to Zoe, an astrophysicist (and someone much brainier than the audience) from the twenty-first century, just what a candle was!

The Second Doctor also seemed to have less purpose than his predecessor. The First Doctor battled with his errant TARDIS to return his companions to their relevant homes (at least to start with). This younger-looking incarnation, whilst equally out of control of the craft, preferred to simply drift from place to place, time to time, with no real purpose, and his companions seemed equally happy with this arrangement. Ben and Polly's return to Earth, on the day they originally left, was a total accident, and although her adventures with the Doctor alarmed her, Victoria settled down seventy-five years after her time quite happily, simply because her experiences with the Doctor taught her much about the late twentieth century.

The television production team of the time saw the Second Doctor as a sort of space tramp, the infamous Cosmic Hobo, who could go anywhere, anytime and settle in quite easily, and breeze out just as simply. By using that idea, making the Doctor more of a casual explorer instead of travelling lecturer, it gave the programme a much needed lease of life and refired the enthusiasm of the viewers. However, after three years, the signs of disinterest were showing again and it was decided another boost was needed.

THE EXILED ADVENTURER

The Third Doctor's era nearly failed to materialise. Six years is a long time in television and few shows in the Sixties survived that long. The BBC were apparently keen to drop the programme and spend their money elsewhere, but luckily for us, nothing suitable reared its head and so a further, but much shorter series of *Doctor Who* was required.

Patrick Troughton and the actors portraying his companions had all been written out at the end of 1969 and a whole new approach was needed. The United Nations Intelligence Task Force – UNIT – had been established during the final Troughton season and was very successful, as indeed were stories set on contemporary Earth. Therefore a decision was made – the Third Doctor would be exiled to Earth and set up base with Brigadier Lethbridge-Stewart and the men and women of UNIT. Of course, this was a complete *volte face* to the Troughton Doctor who would have turned his nose up at officialdom. Even the imperious First Doctor was vaguely condemnatory of military might, so this Third Doctor had to be a character who could fit in with UNIT without necessarily accepting its military regime. Enter Jon Pertwee, a highly talented actor and entertainer, best known for comedy and determined to go against type and play *Doctor Who* totally straight. His Doctor, however, still mirrored the image of the Seventies – a time where the happy–go-lucky fun of the Sixties was giving way to the eventual doldrums of the Eighties.

The *Doctor Who* of the mid Seventies reflected the image of some of its Sixties rivals in many ways, such as *The Avengers* and James Bond – tongue in cheek drama where the establishment fought against outrageous villains and situations. Pertwee saw his character go through many stylistic changes; the first series saw a very serious, moralistic Doctor fighting menaces but with a determination to see all sides of the story. This was no doubt helped by his excellent assistant, a member of UNIT's science corps called Liz Shaw. However when Liz left, the Bridgadier replaced her with a much younger, dizzy blonde called Jo Grant. Jo stayed with the Doctor for the next three years, making their teaming one of the most successful of all time. The Doctor became much more a father figure to both her and the audience.

In addition to softening the Doctor's character, his battles against Earth (and indeed eventually unearthly) bureaucracy became more fierce and more tongue-in-

The Third Doctor spent much time and energy seeking to end his exile on Earth, imposed by the Time Lords. Photo © BBC.

cheek. As well as alien of the week, there was frequently politician of the week to battle!

For his final season, after five years, the Third Doctor returned to the more science based character of his first series. Still as flamboyant, dashing and witty, the Doctor seemed to have matured a lot more, become less tolerant of would be world conquerors and quicker to want to punch the alien on the nose rather than discuss philosophy with it.

A BOHEMIAN AIR

When the Fourth Doctor appeared, all the traits of the previous persona vanished almost overnight. Gone was the father figure, gone was the lightweight antidisestablishmentarianism. In its place the audience found a darker, more brooding and obviously alien figure. Tom Baker used his considerable stature and presence to great effect during the first three of his seven years of portraying the Doctor. He was still against authority, but now far more anarchistic, like an over zealous student, striding purposefully around, making puns and quips whilst his brain worked overtime to solve all and every problem thrown at it.

The search for an actor to replace the phenomenally successful Jon Pertwee was a long and arduous one for the producers. They needed someone who would effortlessly step into Pertwee's shoes and be immediately acceptable and at the same time give the programme a huge boost into yet another direction.

The first thing that had to be done was to sever ties as painlessly as possible with the familiar, cosy world of UNIT. Ironically, in attempting to do this, the producers – unsure when the scripts were being written as to the age and physical ability of a new Doctor – gave the time traveller a secondary companion, Harry Sullivan, a member of UNIT, alongside Sarah Jane Smith, who had joined the Third Doctor in his final stories.

Tom Baker's eventual casting made the Harry character severely redundant and the butt of much college-style humour. He was written out after just one season, along with the Brigadier's character, so that by his second series, the Doctor was, bar the odd fleeting return, very much a traveller in space and time once again, cut off from his home and his people. Ironically, it was the return to his people's home that severed the last tie with contemporary Earth for many years when the Doctor rather unceremoniously dumped Sarah Jane on Earth because he couldn't take her to Gallifrey, his own planet.

The Tom Baker years of *Doctor Who* were by far the most popular ever, not just in the United Kingdom but in the United States where after previous abortive attempts to sell the programme, Baker's mix of unearthly mystery and terribly British humour caught the Americans' imagination just as *The Avengers* had nearly ten years before. In Britain however, the Fourth Doctor's last few years saw a decline in the character's fortunes. Complaints about the content of the show meant the BBC felt it necessary to tone down the darker side of *Doctor Who*, replacing the mystery, suspense, horror and wit with a bizarre, sometimes slapstick. humour.

After a moderately successful experiment giving the Doctor a totally savage, instinctive companion, the BBC producers went the other way and gave the Fourth Doctor an intellectual equal, Romana, a Time Lord like himself. Romana, and the Doctor's mobile computer, K9 ceased to be the traditional foils for the Doctor to explain the plot to, because they usually knew what was going on at the same time, if not before the Doctor did! This left many viewers feeling they were peeping in on a rather exclusive comedy programme aimed above their heads, rather than an action and adventure series they could participate in. As the programme entered the Eighties however, in the Fourth Doctor's final series, changes were made.

A FRESH FACE

The boom in fantasy films during the latter end of the seventies had an enormous impact on the programme. Flimsy 'cardboard' sets and rubber monsters had to give way to more sophisticated electronic effects. Likewise, to counter this technological age, the viewer had to be brought back into the prog- ➤

The Bohemian Fourth Doctor, played by Tom Baker takes the series by storm. Naval Doctor Harry Sullivan (Ian Marter) is helpless. Photo © BBC.

ramme, rather than watching from a distance. Companions were changed, the superbrains of K9 and Romana dispatched and replaced by the children, Nyssa and Adric. Later, they were joined by the very Earthy, brash and argumentative Australian Tegan, always there to put a spanner in the works. If Nyssa or Adric asked the Doctor what was happening, Tegan would ask why it was happening and more importantly, why had the Doctor made it happen to them! To finalise this new, hopefully more 'user-friendly' approach, a Fifth Doctor was created.

Peter Davison was as different from Tom Baker as Baker had been from Jon Pertwee. The early Eighties were a time for optimism and adventure in Britain after the dreary Seventies. The new Doctor reflected this: young, dynamic and inquisitive, his innocent looks belying his methodical and quick brain. The Fifth Doctor became more of an older brother rather than father figure or eccentric uncle of earlier incarnations. Gone too was the cliquish wit, in its place a feckless charm designed to talk the Doctor out of trouble rather than bluff his way.

In many ways the Fifth Doctor was potentially doomed before he started – the unwise choice of an

Brash, arrogant but still popular with many fans – Colin Baker as the doomed Sixth Doctor in *Vengeance on Varos*. Photo © BBC.

established family–recognisable actor like Peter Davison made it difficult to think of him as the Doctor. The youngsters of the Eighties were also expecting a Luke Skywalker (of *Star Wars* fame) type of hero, something *Doctor Who* never has been, nor should it be. The BBC also made a huge mistake by taking the programme out of its Saturday night tea time schedule

and putting it on week nights, twice a week. They seem to have mistaken the high ratings due to Peter Davison for high ratings due to the programme's inherent popularity. When the Fifth Doctor used up the last reserves of his charm and innocence to save his new companion, Peri Brown, the BBC used up the last of the viewing populace's goodwill.

A BOMBASTIC NATURE

The Sixth Doctor echoed the mid-Eighties far too well – dark, antagonistic and basically unlikeable. This Doctor was again radically different from his earlier incarnations. Gone was the approachable trustworthiness, the ability to say that no matter how the Doctor was acting, the viewer knew that all would come right eventually, the Doctor knew what he was doing. Instead, the viewer met an erratic, almost schizoid personality, one minute laughing and joking, the next destroying an enemy with a savagery his previous selves would have expected from their foes.

Colin Baker struggled bravely against this character, injecting humour and charm wherever possible. He always attempted to show the audience that everything was all right .really, and the Doctor they knew and loved was still there, hidden underneath the bravado, waiting for the cue to shine out. The cue never came because the BBC pulled the rug out from under Baker's feet, removing him and the Sixth Doctor overnight, never allowing the actor to portray the Doctor the way he wanted to.
Seeing the programme's popularity fading, the BBC's controllers blamed the actor for the failure rather than themselves for their higgledy piggledy scheduling.

A younger man takes the helm – and companions. Peter Davison leads his crew in *The Visitation*. Photo © BBC.

A RETURN TO MYSTERY

Enter the Seventh and, to date, final television incarnation to be seen so far. If the Sixth Doctor equalled the dark days of the mid-Eighties, the Seventh Doctor pulled right away from any such comparisons. This incarnation really is the oft-quoted but rarely met claim of being a mixture of the other personas, possesing the authority of the First Doctor, the rebel of the Second and the flair for adventure and danger of the Third. He takes the alien mystery of the Fourth, the charm of the Fifth and the occasional darkness of the Sixth, mixing them in a highly enjoyable pot pourri.

Sylvester McCoy, like Jon Pertwee was most recognisable as a showman rather than a serious actor when he came to the role, but his anarchic wit and alternative humour background, along with his proven high level of acting prove beyond doubt that he is exactly right to

What next for the Doctor and Ace? The time travellers contemplate their fate in *Survival*. Photo © BBC.

further the character of The Doctor.

Without doubt the latest Doctor is once again an enigma, hinting that his adventures over the years have perhaps evolved him above the status of being just a renegade Time Lord. Indeed, he may have been playing both the viewer and his fellow Gallifreyans along as to who exactly he is – what his role in the

Universe might be and just how long he has been around. With the strong willed but vulnerable and enthusiastic Ace at his side the future for the Doctor, if not *Doctor Who* the programme, looks set to be very interesting and exciting. Let's hope that when the stories continue, we are all there to be able to enjoy them...

WHO IS THE DOCTOR?

A question asked for many years by many thousands of viewers worldwide! When he first appeared the Doctor was simply a traveller in time and space, cut off from his own world with his grand daughter, Susan. His ship, which is 'dimensionally transcendental' – bigger on the inside than the outside – was disguised as a British Police Box. It seems to be stuck in that form, its 'chameleon circuits' inoperative.

For the followers of the Doctor's early adventures he was very much a mystery man and his regeneration at the end of his first encounter with the Cybermen came as a great surprise. Before his companions very eyes, the Doctor became a new man, with a different body, a different character but the same keen, exploring mind. It was not until the end of this Doctor's 'life' that the time traveller revealed his true nature – a renegade Time Lord.

The seemingly omnipotent Time Lords of the planet Gallifrey maintain a strict policy of non-interference in the lives of other races (the result of events in their early history), only observing the millions of events taking place at every

point in the time-space continuum. The Doctor tired of this life and stole his ship, a TARDIS, setting out to explore the universe himself.

Eventually, the Time Lords caught up with him when he was forced to call on their help to send thousands of Earth soldiers back to their home world at the end of the War Games, a hideous bid for universal power concocted by an alien race. The Doctor was exiled to Earth, his knowledge of time travel blocked, his TARDIS immobilised, his features changed.

Eventually he was reprieved and during his wanderings and further regenerations we learnt more about the Time Lord race and the Doctor's past. In addition, followers of the Doctor encountered other renegade Time Lords, such as Morbius and, of course, the villainous Master who has often appeared to cause trouble.

During his Seventh regeneration, the Doctor seems to have recalled more of his past than he previously cared to admit – a darker past, in which the Doctor may have been one of those alongside the creator of Gallifreyan time technology, Rassilon, when that power was first realised. As the Doctor continues to struggle against evil and injustice, his

A return to mystery? Sylvester McCoy takes centre stage as the Seventh Doctor. Photo © BBC.

actual identity has once again become more of a mystery. Who is this wanderer in the fourth dimension? The answer to that question has yet to be revealed...

Future Imperfect

The TARDIS took only seconds to reform, slotting its misty dimensions through each other until its familiar interior solidified around the travellers.

"Oh, my word!" exclaimed the Doctor, rummaging through his multitude of pockets. "Oh, no! What have I done with it?"

From a cupboard, he hurriedly exracted a battered metal headset, and pulled it over his tousled mop of brown Beatle hair.

"Wait there! I shan't be long," he said to Jamie and Zoe. They stood mouths gaping, as he sat cross-legged on the floor with every appearance of going nowhere at all.

He closed his eyes and stared into the well of imagination that opened before his piercing thoughts. A dark void where the last ideas stolen by the Master of the Land of Fiction, tumbled and escaped. He glimpsed Lancelot and Rapunzel; once again the Minotaur reared above him; but even he, the Doctor, was no more than an idea in this nowhere.

He searched, but found no sign of the thing he had lost.

At last, as his hopes began to fail, he imagined a figure rising like a shade before him. The face was familiar. He recognised the tricorn and pigtailed hair of the fellow traveller immediately.

"My dear Gulliver!" he cried. "And I thought I'd missed the long talk we were to have."

The gentleman smiled. "My only concern is, that I do justice to my master's arguments and expression."

"Ah well, that might be a little difficult. You see, your master no longer exists."

Gulliver shook his head. "But how can this be?"

"Let's just say we had a slight literary disagreement."

The Doctor would have thrown his arms wide, had his thoughts had arms. "And now you're free to go!"

This seemed to cheer the traveller and he asked "To gratify that insatiable desire to see the world in every period of antiquity placed before me? How like you, Doctor."

"Yes," laughed the Doctor, but he felt a momentary twinge of puzzlement. "There is one thing though. I don't suppose you've seen my recorder, have you? About so long . . ." Again, in frustration, he had no way of measuring it.

Gulliver gave the strangest look. "I had learned in my youth to play a little upon the spinet," he said. "But you Doctor, what else do you play?"

Lost thoughts scattered mockingly around them in the void. Imagination played terrible tricks, "Dean Swift never wrote that," said the Doctor coldly.

"Indeed?" said the gentleman.

"No." The Doctor stared at the familiar face. "But I know you from somewhere."

"Perhaps."

The uneasiness he felt was growing steadily. "Oh, yes . . . I mean, no! I mean, you're not Gulliver at all!"

That face. Long ago, he had seen it, presiding over hearings at the Celestial Intervention Agency.

"My mistake," he exclaimed. "Goodbye!" And he tried to wake up.

"No, Doctor! You are required . . ."

"You're from the Time Lords." His stomach churned. "I'm nothing to do with you any more!"

"Doctor!"

"No! I won't stay! I won't be locked up by you and your boring, bureaucratic . . . inkslingers!"

"That time is long in your future. And long in our past."

"I know you. Your name's Geth, or Goth, or something . . . Why don't you stay out of my business!"

"Doctor, whatever our respective pasts and futures, the Time Lords need you now. No one else can be spared."

"Need me? With all your high and mighty powers? Oh, no! This is a trap . . ."

A vision came upon the Doctor. Energy from a onced blazing star dwindled into a pit of darkness. His home world, epitome of everything staid and smug and all-powerful, crumbled and teetered on the brink of destruction.

And they were pleading for his help?

"Oh dear. You are in a pickle, aren't you?" he said. "And just supposing I do help. . . ?"

"Then you go free, Doctor . . . eventually."

"Eventually?" he shouted. "What does that mean?"

But he found himself already returned to the TARDIS, and it was stangely changed.

A tall white-haired figure indulgently overdressed in red, stared at him across his time rotor. A young lady in blue was holding his missing recorder.

"Thank you very much," said the Doctor, resigned to his fate. "I was looking for that."

Marc Platt

"...IT'S ALL SO MUCH JUNK! I DON'T BELIEVE IT..."

HOW CAN ONE MAN COLLECT UP SO MUCH CLUTTER?

TALKING TO YOURSELF NOW, ACE?

CAUGHT ME AT IT, DOCTOR. WHAT DO THEY SAY AGAIN?

...FIRST SIGN OF MADNESS?

SOMETIMES, IT'S THE FIRST SIGN OF DANGER...

IF YOU'RE OFF FOR A JOG DOWN MEMORY LANE...

... I'D LIKE TO JOIN YOU.

HEH HEH...VERY WELL, THEN. IF YOU'RE SITTING COMFORTABLY...

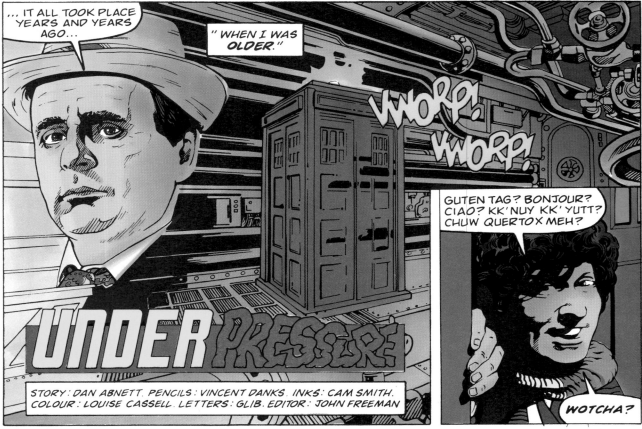

... IT ALL TOOK PLACE YEARS AND YEARS AGO...

"WHEN I WAS OLDER."

VWORP! VWORP!

GUTEN TAG? BONJOUR? CIAO? KK'NUY KK'YUTT? CHUW QUERTOX MEH?

WOTCHA?

UNDER PRESSURE

STORY: DAN ABNETT. PENCILS: VINCENT DANKS. INKS: CAM SMITH. COLOUR: LOUISE CASSELL. LETTERS: GLIB. EDITOR: JOHN FREEMAN

AHOY THERE, MATEY! ERM...

.. TAKE ME TO YOUR LEADER?

... NINE DEGREES PORT, DEPTH EIGHT HUNDRED, **MISTER HARDY**. TAKE US IN ALONG THE VALLEY FLOOR.

HELM-NINE DEGREES PORT, DEPTH EIGHT HUNDRED, AYE SIR.

COMMUNICATIONS! ANY JOY FROM THE SURFACE YET?

STILL NOTHING, SIR. VIDEO'S BLANK, AND THERE'S JUST WHITE NOISE ON THE RADIO. IF THE JUTLAND'S STILL UP THERE IN THAT STORM, SHE'S KEEPING AWFULLY QUIET.

DAMMIT, MAN. THIS WHOLE OPER-ATION'S GOING TO PIECES! OUR ORDERS STATED EXPLICITLY THAT DIRECT REFERENCE TO THE **EXPERT** ON BOARD THE JUTLAND WAS NECESSARY AT EVERY STAGE. WE CAN'T CONTINUE UNTIL...

WHAT ON EARTH IS THAT?

...FIFTEEN MEN ON A DEAD MAN'S CHEST, YO HO HO AND A BOTTLE OF RUM...

... DRINK AND THE DEVIL HAD ... GOOD DAY!

HALLIDAY! WHAT'S THE MEANING OF THIS? WHO IS THIS MAN?

DON'T KNOW, SIR! FOUND HIM IN THE AFT ENGINE COMPANIONWAY KNOCKING ON THE WALLS. HE—

COME COME, NOW! I REALLY CAN'T BELIEVE THIS...

... SURELY IT'S VERY IRREGULAR...

QUENELL M.F. CAPTAIN

"... CAPTAIN *QUENELL* THAT AFTER ..."

MISSION TIME
32:14

"... NEARLY A DAY AND A HALF INTO THE OPERATION HERE ..."

"... NINETY MILES OFF LOWESTOFT, YOU DON'T RECOGNISE ..."

... THE *SCIENTIFIC ADVISOR* SECONDED TO THIS OPERATION?

WOULDN'T YOU SAY?

I CAN'T BELIEVE I WOULDN'T BE AWARE OF MY OWN SHIP'S COMPLIMENT. THIS OPERATION'S SCIENTIFIC ADVISOR, MISTER -

DOCTOR.

- DOCTOR, IS ABOARD OUR SUPPORT VESSEL ON THE SURFACE.

QUITE SURE ABOUT THAT?

I DON'T LIKE YOUR TONE ONE BIT. HALLIDAY, CONFINE HIM TO - *WHAT DO YOU THINK YOU'RE DOING?*

CURIOUS. WE'RE NOT A MILLION MILES AWAY FROM POOR OLD OIL RIG ZXT 413.

THE ZXT 413 INCIDENT IS CLASSIFIED. HOW DO YOU KNOW...

I WAS THERE... JUST ABOUT. THIS OPERATION IS TO DO WITH *SEA DEVILS* ISN'T IT?

HOW DO YOU KNOW ALL THIS?

AS I SAID. I'M AN EXPERT... AND I DARE SAY...

...VITAL TO THIS MISSION.

I DON'T KNOW. I THINK PERHAPS -

-UHHNG!

CAPTAIN!

KLUD!

AHH!

COMMUNICATIONS, TRY RAISING THE JUTLAND AGAIN.

ARE YOU REALLY OUR SCIENTIFIC ADVISOR, DOCTOR?

LOOKS LIKE IT...

...AND ARE YOU REALLY FIRST OFFICER *HARDY?* WHEN DO I MEET ENSIGN *BLIGH,* ADMIRAL *NELSON* AND CHIEF PETTY OFFICER *LONG JOHN SILVER?*

JUTLAND, JUTLAND... THIS IS HMS TEMPEST BELOW YOU AT NINE HUNDRED METRES. COME IN PLEASE, JUTLAND. WE HAVE A CODE RED SITUATION... I SAY AGAIN...

SKKKRK!-LAND. THIS IS JUTLAND, COME IN TEMPEST, OVER.

SIR! SIR!

THIS IS TEMPEST. SOMETHING HIT US, JUTLAND. AFT DAMAGE AND SEVERAL CREW HURT, INCLUDING THE CAPTAIN. WHERE WERE YOU, OVER?

BAD WEATHER UP HERE, TEMPEST. RADIO INOP FOR A WHILE THERE. REPEAT YOUR SITUATION. WE'RE PATCHING THROUGH THE SCIENTIFIC ADVISOR, OVER.

TEMPEST. THIS IS THE *DOCTOR* SPEAKING. DO YOU KNOW WHAT HIT YOU. OVER?

DOCTOR?

OH DEAR. OH DEAR ME...

...THIS REALLY DOES MAKE EVERYTHING RATHER MORE DIFFICULT THAN I IMAGINED.

"YOU SEE, ACE, EVERYONE THOUGHT THE PROBLEM LAY WITH THE MYSTERIOUS FORCES ON THE SEA BED, BUT THAT WASN'T THE WHOLE OF IT..."

TEMPEST. THIS IS THE DOCTOR. I SAY AGAIN, DO YOU KNOW WHAT HIT YOU, OVER?

IT'S NO GOOD, JO. THEY'VE GONE AGAIN.

I THINK MY STOMACH MIGHT GO AGAIN IN A MINUTE TOO, DOCTOR.

"...ON THE SURFACE SHIP WAS MY PREVIOUS INCARNATION, A REAL DANDY OF A FELLOW, AND THAT WASN'T GOOD AT ALL..."

NOW NOW, OLD GIRL. YOU'LL GET YOUR SEA LEGS EVENTUALLY.

"...THE FRAIL STRUCTURE OF TIME DOESN'T ENTERTAIN A PARADOX LIKE THAT HAPPILY..."

"WHY NOT?"

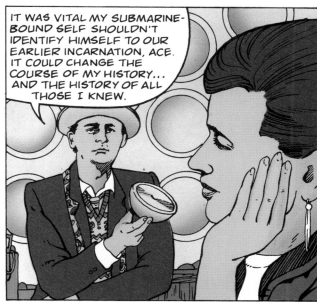

IT WAS VITAL MY SUBMARINE-BOUND SELF SHOULDN'T IDENTIFY HIMSELF TO OUR EARLIER INCARNATION, ACE. IT COULD CHANGE THE COURSE OF MY HISTORY... AND THE HISTORY OF ALL THOSE I KNEW.

BUT BY THE SAME TOKEN, I COULDN'T JUST SLIP AWAY AND LEAVE MY EARLIER SELF TO IT.

I COULD REMEMBER CLEARLY, YOU SEE, HOW AN UNKNOWN MEMBER OF THE SUB'S CREW HAD HELPED SOLVE THAT CRISIS WITH THE SEA DEVILS...

"...I HAD BECOME A CRUCIAL PART OF MY OWN PAST. AND I HAD TO PLAY OUT THAT PART EXACTLY..."

"...OR DIE TRYING."

...COME IN TEMPEST, THIS IS THE DOCTOR. COME IN TEMPEST...

CONTINUED ON PAGE 45.

Time on a Vine

The last one took her down and she hit the ground, hard. She managed to make it back up onto her knees, but that was about as far as it went; she stayed there half-crouched and with her head lowered, certain that they would be coming at her again in a matter of seconds. As she waited for the attack she could feel the strange, gritty dust under her fingers like grains of black rubber, resembling no other soil that she'd ever seen. Her long hair was matted with blood after the repeated attacks of the past three days, and it hung around her face like a curtain.

They could have her now. She had no strength left, no will to go on.

They'd come out of the sky whenever she'd tried to cover the distance from the rocks to the desert pool; they looked like birds but they slashed like razors and were completely without mercy. They seemed to have only one purpose, and that was to cut her off from the only source of water for miles around.

She waited for the attack.

But the attack never came.

Instead, a hand gripped her arm. Three days ago, when all of this had begun, an unexpected touch would almost certainly have startled her. She'd have whooped, shrieked, maybe even jumped. But now she just stared down at it, dully. A man's hand. A pale coat sleeve.

"Try to stand," a voice suggested.

She looked up into his face. A young man's face. Straw-blond hair, pleasant features, a smile that reassured and invited trust and which seemed to say *It's all right, I understand.* Nothing in it that could ever inspire unease.

"*Can* you get up?" he said. "If not, I can carry you."

She looked toward the pool. After three days of dehydration she doubted whether she could speak, let alone explain herself; her throat was too dry even to swallow and her lips felt as if they would crack like old slate.

She rose. And like a driven thing, her body tried to take another step toward the water that had been so close and yet so unreachable for so long. Whatever this place was, it seemed to have no night. Her expensive wristwatch kept the time and changed the date, but both concepts appeared to be meaningless in these new surroundings. The only relief from the pitiless sun had been the shade of the rocks; shade that had been so welcome at first, but which had slowly become her prison.

"No!" he said quickly, and swung her away. He did it with ease. She seemed to have no weight. She took one staggering step with his support, and then she flinched in anticipation of what always happened next.

After a moment, she squinted up at the sky. They were circling there still.

But they weren't coming down.

"It isn't water," he said. "I know it's hard to believe, but it's an illusion. They won't harm you as long as you don't try to approach it. They weren't protecting the pool. They were protecting *you*."

He was leading her now, one staggering step after another, toward the ridgeline. And, exactly as he'd said, no attack seemed to be coming.

Her voice was a whisper, *"Is it poisoned?"*

"Something worse than poison," he said.

She almost fell, but he righted her. They were descending now. About a hundred yards downslope of them stood an absurd blue box. Absurd, because it didn't belong here; it was a police box, the kind that they'd abandoned back in the days when the police had acquired more up-to-date technology and which radiated a kind of old-world familiarity in these hostile surroundings.

"You'll need more than just water," he said. 'You're low on body salts and electrolytes. I'd have reached you sooner if I could, but this place isn't easy to get to. I had to take the best window available.'

"I don't understand," she said.

"I know. Don't worry."

She wanted to tell him. About this nightmare. That was what she'd called it, at first, when she'd stepped through the door into what was supposed to be a high-powered client meeting on the fifteenth floor of the agency building. She'd been psyched-up, she'd been ready; but as she'd stepped through the door it had been to find herself faced, not with the conference room and the usual half-dozen suits, but with this.

"There's a lot to explain," he said, as he raised his other hand and sent ahead some kind of signal that caused the door of the police box to open in silence; she could see that he'd brought along her portfolio, and she wondered why. It had seemed laughably irrelevant under this new set of circumstances, and after the first twelve hours of the nightmare she'd abandoned it by the rocks.

He said, "You were pulled from your timeline and abandoned here. Deliberately. The intention was that you should never be found. You were about to set out a very persuasive business plan to a group of executives who aren't aware that the entire future of their company depends on how they react to your advice. There's a discovery waiting two hundred years down the line that'll help to change the course of a major interspecies war, and without you there's no chance that it will ever be made."

He was guiding her into the box. And instead of darkness and confinement ahead of her, she saw light and space.

"Can you..."

"Take you back? That's the idea. But some things are already beginning to run out of control. There's a lot to be done before you can pick up again where you left off, and I'm going to need your help."

She looked at him then, seeking reassurance in the midst of what sounded like madness. A friendly smile. A young man's face.

But not a young man's eyes at all.

She stood at the door, and reached for the handle. She was thirty seconds late.

No-one would ever know. Nobody could even begin to imagine some of the things that she'd seen and done in more than a year and a half of what could only be called, under the circumstances, subjective time.

And it hurt.

It wasn't because of the danger. Cut off as she'd been from her life and any sense of her own future, her fears and her notions of safety had undergone a significant change. Nothing would ever scare her in quite the same way again, even though she was back almost exactly at the point where she'd started –

same clothes, hair as close as she could get it, her portfolio showing only the faintest mark from where she'd used it to jam the treads on the advancing Warboy when the Big One had been coming down...

But on the inside, so much was different.

There had been a moment. Just one. When she'd thought that it might be possible to go on forever, when she'd dared to think that the past to which she'd longed to return might actually have less of a hold on her than the future which could lie ahead.

And then he'd told her of the others.

Teela, Tegan, Leela, Zoe, Romana, Nyssa, Victoria... she could barely remember a fraction of the names that he'd mentioned, although it was clear to her that he had very precise memories of every one of them. And she'd realised that she'd have to face what each of them, in turn, must have faced.

That forever is a relative term. And that for some, forever is over much sooner than for others.

And in that, she believed that she'd sensed the heart of the sadness that she'd always perceived in him. There was no flower in the garden that would not wither and die in his hands within moments of being picked. He would never have any choice. He could only move on.

Such a young man's face.

But not a young man's eyes at all.

She got a good grip on her portfolio. She got an even better grip on herself.

And then she opened the door and stepped forward into the conference room.

John Lydecker

The Complete Guide

Twenty-eight years after it began, *Doctor Who* has seen nearly two hundred television adventures and innumerable spin-off stories in books, comic strip and audio form. Included in the list below are pertinent production details, ratings per episode and information on the story if a major character or monster is introduced or a new technique is used in the filming.

Legend: The title of the story is listed first, followed by alternative titles in brackets where there's some dispute. This applies mainly to the early Hartnell stories, which had individual episode titles until the story *The Savages* (Story AA) which we do not have space to list. The Production Code (eg. AA) precedes the story title. The number of episodes in the story follows the first transmission details.

Symbols: Tx First transmission date for the story as BBC1 in England. **R** Average rating (in millions, based on the total viewers for each episode – first transmission figures only) **Wr** Writer **Dr** Director **Dgr** Designer. Symbols: ● Novelisation available from W. H. Allen. ○ Novelisation unavailable. ◆ BBC Video available in Britain. ◇ Video unavailable. ▲ Complete in BBC Archive. △ Incomplete in format for United Kingdom transmission. For further details, see separate table. Where Producers and Script Editors change, these have been listed above the first story where the change occurs.

The First Doctor (1963-1966)

Played by William Hartnell

Season One

Producer: Verity Lambert
Associate Producer: Mervyn Pinfield
Story Editor: David Whitaker
Doctor Who created by Sydney Newman and Donald Wilson (uncreditted)

A *AN UNEARTHLY CHILD*
(*100,000BC* or *The Tribe of Gum*)
Tx 23/11/63 – 14/12/63: Four Episodes ● ◆ ▲
R 5.9 millions **Wr** Anthony Coburn (and C. E. Webber, uncredited) **Dr** Waris Hussein **Dgr** Peter Brachaki (Ep. 1, *An Unearthly Child*) and Barry Newbery

Two schoolteachers, Ian Chesterton (William Russell) and Barbara Wright (Jacqueline Hill), accidentally discover the TARDIS in a junkyard at 76 Totters Lane, London. Together with the Doctor (William Hartnell) and his grand-daughter Susan (Carole Ann Ford) they are thrown back in time and encounter a stone-age tribe that has lost the secret of making fire.

B *THE DALEKS*
(*The Mutants* or *The Survivors*)
Tx 21/12/63 – 1/2/64: Seven ● ◆ ▲
R 9.0 **Wr** Terry Nation **Dr** Christopher Barry (Eps 1, 2, 4, 5), Richard Martin (Eps 3, 6, 7) **Dgr** Raymond P. Cusick (Eps 1-5, 7), Jeremy Davies (Ep 6)
First appearance of the Daleks, who seemed to be killed off on their planet of origin, Skaro, leaving the Thals triumphant. This

story was adapted to become Doctor Who and the Daleks, *an Amicus film starring Peter Cushing as Doctor Who.*

C *THE EDGE OF DESTRUCTION*
(*Inside the Spaceship* or *Beyond the Sun*)
Tx 8/2/64 – 15/2/64: Two ● ◇ ▲
R 10.2 **Wr** David Whitaker **Drs** Richard Martin (Ep 1), Frank Cox (Ep 2) **Dgr** Raymond P. Cusick

★ *Doctor Who* made its earliest appearance on BBC Television on 16th November 1963 at 5.41pm in a promotional trailer for *An Unearthly Child* which featured the dematerialisation sequence from the episode.

D *MARCO POLO*
Tx 22/2/64 – 4/4/64: Seven ● ◇ △
R 9.5 **Wr** John Lucarotti **Dr** Waris Hussein (1-3, 5-7) and John Crockett (Ep 4) **Dgr** Barry Newbery
E *THE KEYS OF MARINUS*
Tx 11/4/64 – 16/5/64: Six ● ◇ ▲
R 9.1 **Wr** Terry Nation **Dr** John Gorrie **Dgr** Raymond P. Cusick
F *THE AZTECS*
Tx 23/5/64 – 13/6/64: Four ● ◇ ▲
R 7.5 **Wr** John Lucarotti **Dr** John Crockett **Dgr** Barry Newbery

G *THE SENSORITES*
Tx 20/6/64 – 1/8/64: Six ● ◇ ▲
R 6.9 **Wr** Peter P. Newman **Dr** Mervyn Pinfield (Eps 1-4), Frank Cox (Eps 5, 6) **Dgr** Raymond P. Cusick
H *THE REIGN OF TERROR*
Tx 8/8/64 – 12/9/64: Six ● ◇ △
R 6.7 **Wr** Dennis Spooner **Dr** Henric Hirsch (Timothy Combe, Ep 6, uncredited) **Dgr** Roderick Laing

★ The Daleks first appeared – in part – at the very end of *The Daleks: The Dead Planet*. The episode *The Ambush* was the first to be transmitted off a 35mm telerecording as opposed to videotape.

Season Two

◄ J PLANET OF GIANTS
Tx 31/10/64 – 14/11/64: Three ●◇▲
R 8.6 **Wr** Louis Marks **Dr** Mervyn Pinfield
(Eps 1, 2), Douglas Camfield (Ep 3) **Dgr**
Raymond P. Cusick
K THE DALEK INVASION OF EARTH
Tx 21/11/64 – 26/12/64: Six ●◆▲
R 11.9 **Wr** Terry Nation **Dr** Richard Martin
Dgr Spencer Chapman
*Susan leaves as the Doctor defeats the
Daleks who have invaded Earth, intent on
turning it into a giant spaceship by removing
its magnetic core. Filmed as* Daleks:
Invasion Earth 2150AD *with Peter Cushing as
Doctor Who.*

Story Editor: Dennis Spooner

★ The first novelization based on the
series was *Doctor Who in an
Exciting Adventure With the Daleks*
by David Whitaker and published by
Frederick Muller in November 1964.
The first paperback edition came
from Armada the following October.

L THE RESCUE
Tx 2/1/65 – 9/1/65: Two ●◇▲
R 12.5 **Wr** David Whitaker **Dr** Christopher
Barry **Dgr** Raymond P. Cusick
*Vicki (Maureen O'Brien) joins the TARDIS
crew, rescued from the planet Dido. She is a
child of the Twenty-Fifth century.*

★ *The Rescue: Desperate Measures*
was the episode which first took the
series into that week's television
Top 10 in terms of ratings. The
previous episode, *The Powerful
Enemy*, featured the first
pseudonym to hide a plot
revelation: Sydney Wilson who was
really Ray Barrett.

M THE ROMANS
Tx 16/1/65 – 6/2/65: Four ●◇▲
R 11.6 **Wr** Dennis Spooner **Dr** Christopher
Barry **Dgr** Raymond P. Cusick

No Associate Producer from here on.

32

*The Daleks' Master Plan: companion Sara Kingdom is killed at its climax, a victim of the Time
Destructor. Photo © Barry Newbery.*

N THE WEB PLANET
Tx 13/2/65 – 20/3/65: Six ●◆▲
R 12.5 **Wr** Bill Strutton **Dr** Richard Martin
Dgr John Wood
P THE CRUSADE
Tx 27/3/65 – 17/4/65: Four ●◇△
R 9.4 **Wr** David Whitaker **Dr** Douglas
Camfield **Dgr** Barry Newbery

★ *Dr Who and the Daleks* was the first
film based on the show to be made
by Aaru for Regal Films. Starring
Peter Cushing as Doctor Who, it was
released on 25th June 1965 and
made its BBC1 debut on 1st July
1972. For the public, it was the first
chance to see an adventure in full
colour.

★ The first *Doctor Who* Annual from
World Distributors appeared in the
Autumn of 1965, featuring
adventures with Zarbi, Voord and
Sensorites.

Q THE SPACE MUSEUM
Tx 24/4/65 – 15/5/65: Four ●◇▲
R 9.2 (incomplete figures, none for Ep. 2:
The Dimensions of Time) **Wr** Glyn Jones **Dr**
Mervyn Pinfield **Dgr** Spencer Chapman

R THE CHASE
Tx 22/5/65 – 26/6/65: Six ●◇▲
R 9.4 **Wr** Terry Nation **Dr** Richard Martin **Dgr**
Raymond P. Cusick and John Wood
*Ian and Barbara leave and return to 1965 in a
Dalek time machine. Steven Taylor (Peter
Purves), a space pilot, makes his first
appearance.*

Story Editor: Donald Tosh

S THE TIME MEDDLER
Tx 3/7/65 – 24/7/65: Four ●◇▲
R 8.4 **Wr** Dennis Spooner **Dr** Douglas
Camfield **Dgr** Barry Newbery
Steven joins.

Season Three

T GALAXY 4
Tx 11/9/65 – 2/10/65: Four ●◇△
R 9.9 **Wr** William Emms **Dr** Derek Martinus
Dgr Richard Hunt
T/A MISSION TO THE UNKNOWN
(Dalek Cutaway)
Tx 9/10/65: One Episode ●◇△
R 8.3 **Wr** Terry Nation **Dr** Derek Martinus
Dgr Richard Hunt, Raymond P. Cusick
*The only episode to date to not have featured
the Doctor or TARDIS crew; a unique trailer
(so far) for the twelve-episode story to
follow.*

Producer: John Wiles

U THE MYTH MAKERS
Tx 16/10/65 – 6/11/65: Four ●◇△
R 8.3 **Wr** Donald Cotton **Dr** Michael Leeston-
Smith **Dgr** John Wood
Vicki leaves. Katarina (Adrienne Hill) joins.

V *THE DALEKS' MASTER PLAN*
Tx 13/11/65 – 29/1/66: Twelve ●◇△
R 9.4 **Wrs** Terry Nation (Eps 1-5, 7) and Dennis Spooner, from an idea by Terry Nation (Eps 6, 8-12) **Dgrs** Raymond Cusick (Eps 1, 2, 5-7, 11), Barry Newbery (Eps 3, 4, 8, 9, 10, 12)
Katarina is killed; Sara Kingdom (Jean Marsh) joins the TARDIS crew but is killed as the Time Destructor ravages the planet Kembel, wrecking the Daleks' conquest plans for the universe.

Script Editor: Gerry Davis
(As indicated from Ep 4 of *The Massacre of St. Bartholemew's Eve: Bell of Doom*)

W *THE MASSACRE OF ST. BARTHOLEMEW'S EVE*
Tx 5/2/66 – 26/2/66: Four ●◇△
R 6.4 **Wr** John Lucarotti (Eps 1-3) and Donald Tosh (Ep 4) **Dr** Paddy Russell **Dgr** Michael Young
Dodo (Jackie Lane) joins from contemporary Earth.

X *THE ARK*
Tx 5/3/66 – 26/3/66: Four ●◇▲
R 6.5 **Wr** Paul Erickson and Lesley Scott **Dr** Michael Imison **Dgr** Barry Newbery

Producer: Innes Lloyd

Y *THE CELESTIAL TOYMAKER*
Tx 2/4/66 – 23/4/66: Four ●◇△
R 8.3 **Wr** Brian Hayles **Dr** Bill Sellars **Dgr** John Wood
Z *THE GUNFIGHTERS*
Tx 30/4/66 – 21/5/66: Four ●◇▲
R 6.2 **Wr** Donald Cotton **Dr** Rex Tucker **Dgr** Barry Newbery

AA *THE SAVAGES*
Tx 28/5/66 – 18/6/66: Four ●◇△
R 4.9 **Wr** Ian Stuart Black **Dr** Christopher Barry **Dgr** Stuart Walker
Steven leaves to become leader of a united race of past masters – the Elders – and the primitive Savages.

BB *THE WAR MACHINES*
Tx 25/6/66 – 16/7/66: Four ●◇▲
R 5.2 **Wr** Ian Stuart Black, from an idea by Kit Pedler **Dr** Michael Ferguson **Dgr** Raymond London
Dodo leaves, Ben Jackson (Michael Craze) and Polly (Anneke Wills) join, both from contemporary Earth.

★ The first 'send-up' of *Doctor Who* came in a sketch from BBC's *Crackerjack* in January 1964 where the Doctor, played by the late Peter Glaze, landed in his TARDIS (a pillar box) to face a Dalek.

★ The first time a TV personality appeared in the show as himself was newsreader Kenneth Kendall in Episode 4 of *The War Machines*.

Season Four
CC *THE SMUGGLERS*
Tx 10/9/66 – 1/10/66: Four ●◇△
R 4.5 **Wr** Brian Hayles **Dr** Julia Smith **Dgr** Richard Hunt

DD *THE TENTH PLANET*
Tx 8/10/66 – 29/10/66: Four ●◇△
R 6.7 **Wr** Kit Pedler (Eps 1, 2) and Kit Pedler and Gerry Davis (Eps 3, 4) **Dr** Derek Martinus **Dgr** Peter Kindred
First appearance of the Cybermen. The Doctor regenerates.

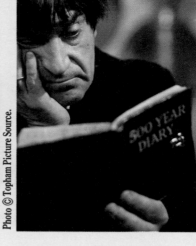

The Second Doctor (1966-1969)
Played by Patrick Troughton

EE *THE POWER OF THE DALEKS*
Tx 5/11/66 – 10/12/66: Six ○◇△
R 7.8 **Wr** David Whitaker **Dr** Christopher Barry **Dgr** Derek Dodd
The rejuvenated Doctor proves his mettle as the space colony Vulcan is threatened.
FF *THE HIGHLANDERS*
Tx 17/12/66 – 7/1/67: Four ●◇△
R 7.0 **Wr** Elwyn Jones and Gerry Davis **Dr** Hugh David **Dgr** Geoffrey Kirkland

Jamie McCrimmon (Frazer Hines) joins, an eighteenth-century Scottish Highlander. The last purely historical story until Black Orchid.
GG *THE UNDERWATER MENACE*
Tx 14/1/67 – 4/2/67: Four ●◇△
R 7.5 **Wr** Geoffrey Orme **Dr** Julia Smith **Dgr** Jack Robinson
HH *THE MOONBASE*
Tx 11/2/67 – 4/3/67: Four ●◇△
R 8.3 **Wr** Kit Pedler **Dr** Morris Barry **Dgr** Colin Shaw
JJ *THE MACRA TERROR*
Tx 11/3/67 – 1/4/67: Four ●◇△
R 8.2 **Wr** Ian Stuart Black **Dr** John Davies **Dgr** Kenneth Sharp

Associate Producer: Peter Bryant ➤

★ *Fury from the Deep* Episode 1 was the first time that the Doctor's sonic screwdriver was featured.

★ The first time a transmission breakdown ever hit an episode was during the repeat of *The Evil of the Daleks* Episode 3, which was the first story repeated in its entirety.

◄ **KK** *THE FACELESS ONES*
Tx 8/4/67 – 13/5/67: Six ● ◇ △
R 7.4 **Wr** David Ellis and Malcolm Hulke **Dr**
Gerry Mill **Dgr** Geoffrey Kirkland
Ben and Polly leave, arriving back on Earth
on exactly the same day as they left.

No Associate Producer from here
Story Editors: Gerry Davis (Eps 1-3) and
Peter Bryant (Eps 2-4)

LL *THE EVIL OF THE DALEKS*
Tx 20/5/67 – 1/7/67: Seven ○ ◇ △
R 6.4 **Wr** David Whitaker **Dr** Derek Martinus
Dgr Chris Thompson
Victoria Waterfield (Deborah Watling) joins
the TARDIS crew after her father is killed as
Skaro, the Daleks' home planet, is plunged
into civil war.

Season Five
Producer: Peter Bryant
Story Editor: Victor Pemberton

MM *THE TOMB OF THE CYBERMEN*
Tx 2/9/67 – 23/9/67: Four Episodes● ◇ △
R 6.8 **Wr** Kit Pedler and Gerry Davis **Dr**
Morris Barry **Dgr** Martin Johnson
The Cybermats are introduced for the first
time, small robotic slaves of the Cybermen

Producer: Innes Lloyd
Story Editor: Peter Bryant

NN *THE ABOMINABLE SNOWMEN*
Tx 30/9/67 – 4/11/67: Six ● ◇ △
R 6.8 **Wr** Mervyn Haisman and Henry
Lincoln **Dr** Gerald Blake **Dgr** Malcolm
Middleton
First Great Intelligence story, first
appearance of the Yeti.

34

OO *THE ICE WARRIORS*
Tx 11/11/67 – 16/12/67: Six ● ◇ △
R 7.3 **Wr** Brian Hayles **Dr** Derek Martinus
Dgr Jeremy Davies
First appearance of the Ice Warriors,
soldiers from the planet Mars.

★ **The first story to have a specially**
produced trailer (i.e. one featuring
material not in the episode) was
The Ice Warriors.

PP *THE ENEMY OF THE WORLD*
Tx 23/12/67 – 27/1/68: Six ● ◇ △
R 7.4 **Wr** David Whitaker **Dr** Barry Letts **Dgr**
Christopher Pemsel
Troughton in a double role as both the
Doctor and the evil Salamander.

Producer: Peter Bryant
Story Editor: Derrick Sherwin

QQ *THE WEB OF FEAR*
Tx 3/2/68 – 9/3/68: Six ● ◇ △
R 7.6 **Wr** Mervyn Haisman and Henry
Lincoln **Dr** Douglas Camfield **Dgr** David
Myerscough-Jones
The Yeti return and Nicholas Courtney
debuts as Colonel Alistair Gordon
Lethbridge-Stewart.
RR *FURY FROM THE DEEP*
Tx 16/3/68 – 20/4/68: Six ● ◇ △
R 7.2 **Wr** Victor Pemberton **Dr** Hugh David
Dgr Peter Kindred
Victoria is adopted by the Harris family.

SS *THE WHEEL IN SPACE*
Tx 27/4/68 – 1/6/68: Six ● ◇ △
R 7.2 **Wr** David Whitaker (from a story by Kit
Pedler) **Dr** Tristan de Vere Cole **Dgr** Derek
Dodd
Victoria is left behind on Earth but Zoe
Herriot (Wendy Padbury) joins, an
astrophysicist with a photographic memory,
as the Doctor fights to defeat another threat
from the Cybermen.

Season Six
Script Editor: Derrick Sherwin

TT *THE DOMINATORS*
Tx 10/8/68 – 7/9/68: Five ● ◆ ▲
R 6.2 **Wr** Norman Ashby (Mervyn
Haisman and Henry Lincoln) **Dr** Morris
Barry **Dgr** Barry Newbery
UU *THE MIND ROBBER*
Tx 14/9/68 – 12/10/68: Five ● ◆ ▲
R 6.9 **Wr** Peter Ling (Eps 2-5); Derrick
Sherwin (Ep 1, uncredited) **Dr** David
Maloney **Dgr** Evan Hercules

Script Editor: Terrance Dicks

VV *THE INVASION*
Tx 2/11/68 – 21/12/68: Eight ● ◇ △
R 6.9 **Wr** Derrick Sherwin, from an idea by
Kit Pedler **Dr** Douglas Camfield **Dgr** Richard
Hunt
The United Nations Intelligence Task Force
(UNIT), led by Brigadier Alistair Gordon
Lethbridge-Stewart, help the Doctor deal
with the Cybermen once more.
First appearance of Benton (John
Levene).
WW *THE KROTONS*
Tx 28/12/68 – 18/1/68: Four ● ◆ ▲
R 8.0 **Wr** Robert Holmes **Dr** David Maloney
Dgr Raymond London
XX *THE SEEDS OF DEATH*
Tx 25/1/69 – 1/3/69: Six ● ◆ ▲
R 7.2 **Wr** Brian Hayles **Dr** Michael Ferguson
Dgr Paul Allen

Script Editor: Derrick Sherwin

YY *THE SPACE PIRATES*
Tx 8/3/69 – 12/4/69: Six Episodes
R 5.9 **Wr** Robert Holmes **Dr** Michael Hart
Dgr Ian Watson

Producer: Derrick Sherwin
Script Editor: Terrance Dicks

ZZ *THE WAR GAMES*
Tx 19/4/69 – 21/6/69: Ten ● ◆ ▲
R 4.9 **Wr** Malcolm Hulke, Terrance Dicks **Dr**
David Maloney **Dgr** Robert Cheveley
Despite defeating the War Chief, the Doctor
is unable to send captured Earth troops back
to their own times and planet on his own.
When he calls his people for help, the time
traveller is forced to surrender to trial for
interfering in the lives of other races. Found
guilty, he is exiled to Earth and his
appearance changed once more. His
companions, Jamie and Zoe, are sent back
to their own times, their memories wiped of
all but their first adventure with the errant
Time Lord...

★ ***The War Games*** **was the first story**
where the Time Lords, the Doctor's
own race, were referred to by name.

The Third Doctor (1970-1974)

Played by Jon Pertwee
Colour Stories begin. Note: for Jon Pertwee's period, **Missing Episodes** refers to those stories **not** currently held in a complete 625VT colour copy format, the type needed for British transmission as per their original Tx. Beta SP Dubs, which can be transmitted are listed. *(Spearhead from Space* is the only story which was filmed and is held as a 16mm colour print). Black and white 16mm film recordings of episodes, made from the original 625VTs are broadcastable and are held for most episodes missing in the 625VT colour format. **Missing Episodes sought** are listed elsewhere in this Year Book! From story 4A (*Robot*) onwards, all stories are held in a format suitable for UK transmission.

Season Seven

Producer: Derrick Sherwin
Script Editor: Terrance Dicks

AAA *SPEARHEAD FROM SPACE*
Tx 3/1/70 - 24/1/70: Four ● ◆ ▲
R 8.2 **Wr** Robert Holmes **Dr** Derek Martinus **Dgr** Paul Allen
The Doctor arrives on Earth and the Autons make their first appearance, directed by the malevolent Nestenes. Liz Shaw (Caroline John) becomes the Doctor's assistant, a research scientist from Cambridge University. The Doctor agrees to work for UNIT as their scientific advisor until he can repair his TARDIS.

Producer: Barry Letts

BBB *DOCTOR WHO AND THE SILURIANS*
Tx 31/1/70 – 14/3/70: Seven ● ◇ △
R 7.7 **Wr** Malcolm Hulke **Dr** Timothy Combe **Dgr** Barry Newbery
First appearance of the Silurians (Eocenes), intelligent reptiles who ruled the Earth sometime during the dinosaur age. The creatures went into hibernation millions of years ago and now seek to reclaim the planet from the upstart ape – Man.

CCC *THE AMBASSADORS OF DEATH*
Tx 21/3/70 - 2/5/70: Seven ● ◇ △
R 7.3 **Wr** David Whitaker (Uncredited script amendments by Malcolm Hulke) **Dr** Michael Ferguson **Dgr** David Myerscough-Jones
DDD *INFERNO*
Tx 9/5/70 - 20/6/70: Seven ● ◇ △ (All 1″ Conversion)
R 5.6 **Wr** Don Houghton **Dr** Douglas Camfield (and various uncredited scenes, Barry Letts, Douglas Camfield) **Dgr** Jeremy Davies

Season Eight

EEE *TERROR OF THE AUTONS*
Tx 2/1/71 - 23/1/71: Four ● ◇ ▲
R 7.9 **Wr** Robert Holmes **Dr** Barry Letts **Dgr** Ian Watson
Despite their non-interference policy, the Time Lords warn the Doctor of the arrival of the evil renegade Time Lord, the Master (played by Roger Delgado), on Earth. Jo(sephine) Grant (Katy Manning) becomes the Doctor's assistant after Liz Shaw has returned to her academic career. First appearance of Captain Mike Yates (Richard Franklin).
FFF *THE MIND OF EVIL*
Tx 30/1/71 - 6/3/71: Six ● ◇ △
R 8.0 **Wr** Don Houghton **Dr** Timothy Combe **Dgr** Raymond London
GGG *THE CLAWS OF AXOS*
Tx 13/3/71 – 3/4/71: Four ● ◇ ▲ (Beta SP Conversion dub)

R 7.4 **Wr** Bob Baker and Dave Martin **Dr** Michael Ferguson **Dgr** Kenneth Sharp
HHH *COLONY IN SPACE*
Tx 10/4/71 - 15/5/71: Six ● ◇ ▲ (Beta SP Conversion dub)
R 8.5 **Wr** Malcolm Hulke **Dr** Michael Briant **Dgr** Tim Gleeson
The Time Lords operate the Doctor's TARDIS by remote control, in order to resolve a plot by the Master to steal a doomsday weapon on a remote planet.
JJJ *THE DÆMONS*
Tx 22/5/71 - 19/6/71: Five ● ◇ △
R 8.3 **Wr** Guy Leopold (Robert Sloman and Barry Letts) **Dr** Christopher Barry **Dgr** Roger Ford
The Master is captured by UNIT.

Season Nine

KKK *DAY OF THE DALEKS*
Tx 1/1/72 - 22/1/72: Four ● ◆ ▲
R 9.6 **Wr** Louis Marks **Dr** Paul Bernard **Dgr** David Myerscough-Jones

MMM *THE CURSE OF PELADON*
Tx 29/1/72 - 19/2/72: Four ● ◇ ▲ (525 Conversion)
R 9.4 **Wr** Brian Hayles **Dr** Lennie Mayne **Dgr** Gloria Clayton
First Peladon story, first appearances of Alpha Centauri and Aggedor.
LLL *THE SEA DEVILS*
Tx 26/2/72 - 1/4/72: Six ● ◇ ▲ (Beta SP Dubs: 1-5 Conversion, 6 off 625)
R 8.2 **Wr** Malcolm Hulke **Dr** Michael Briant **Dgr** Tony Snoaden
First appearance of the Sea Devils, a race of underwater Eocenes (Silurians). The Master escapes confinement. ➤

★ *Doctor Who and the Silurians* **was the first serial to use colour videotape, and also Colour Seperation Overlay (CSO) which first appeared in Episode 4. Bessie, the Doctor's car, made its debut in Episode 1.**

★ **The first paperback books from Target were issued in May 1973, these being reprints of the Sixties Frederick Muller titles.**

◄ **NNN** *THE MUTANTS*
Tx 8/4/72 - 13/5/72: Six ● ◇ ▲ (Beta SP Conversion dub)
R 7.8 **Wr** Bob Baker and Dave Martin **Dr** Christopher Barry **Dgr** Jeremy Bear
OOO *THE TIME MONSTER*
Tx 20/5/72 - 24/6/72: Six ● ◇ ▲ (Beta SP Conversion dub)
R 7.4 **Wr** Robert Sloman **Dr** Paul Bernard **Dgr** Tim Gleeson

Season Ten

RRR *THE THREE DOCTORS*
Tx 30/12/72 - 20/1/73: Four ● ◇ ▲
R 10.3 **Wr** Bob Baker and Dave Martin **Dr** Lennie Mayne **Dgr** Roger Liminton
First appearance of Omega, a Time Lord stellar engineer who assisted in the original experiments that gave Gallifrey power over time and space. Flung into an anti-matter universe he seeks revenge on the Time Lord race and the first three Doctors are united in a bid to stop his plans.

36

PPP *CARNIVAL OF MONSTERS*
Tx 27/1/73 - 17/2/73: Four ● ◇ ▲
R 9.2 **Wr** Robert Holmes **Dr** Barry Letts **Dgr** Roger Liminton
With a new dematerialisation circuit in his possession and the knowledge of the time travel restored, the Doctor once again starts to travel in time and space, accompanied by Jo Grant. Their first adventure lands them in a miniscope, threatened by the powerful Drashigs.

QQQ *FRONTIER IN SPACE*
Tx 24/2/73 - 31/3/73: Six ● ◇ ▲
R 8.0 **Wr** Malcolm Hulke **Dr** Paul Bernard (also David Maloney, last scene). **Dgr** Cynthia Kljuco
The Master returns, attempting to engineer a war between the Earth and Draconian empires in the Twenty-Sixth Century. He is aided by the Ogrons and a surprising ally. . .
SSS *PLANET OF THE DALEKS*
Tx 7/4/73 - 12/5/73: Six ● ◇ △
R 9.7 **Wr** Terry Nation **Dr** David Maloney **Dgr** John Hurst
First appearance of the Thals since The Daleks in 1963.
TTT *THE GREEN DEATH*
Tx 19/5/73 - 23/6/73: Six ● ◇ ▲
R 7.7 **Wr** Robert Sloman **Dr** Michael Briant **Dgr** John Burrowes
The Doctor finds and takes a blue crystal from Metebelis Three. Jo leaves.

Season Eleven

UUU *THE TIME WARRIOR*
Tx 15/12/73 – 5/1/74: Four ● ◆ ▲
R 8.2 **Wr** Robert Holmes **Dr** Alan Bromly **Dgr** Keith Cheetham
The Sontarans debut and Sarah Jane Smith (Elisabeth Sladen) joins the Doctor.

★ *The Time Warrior Part Two was the first occasion on which the Doctor's home planet was named as Gallifrey. Part One also saw the debut of the diamond logo used on the series for many years, and the first slit-scan title sequence.*

WWW *INVASION OF THE DINOSAURS*
(First episode titled *Invasion*)
Tx 12/1/74 - 16/2/74: Six ● ◇ △
R 9.6 **Wr** Malcolm Hulke **Dr** Paddy Russell **Dgr** Richard Morris
XXX *DEATH TO THE DALEKS*
Tx 23/2/74 - 16/3/74: Four ● ◆ △ (Video, Ep.1 Converted)
R 9.4 **Wr** Terry Nation **Dr** Michael Briant **Dgr** Colin Green
YYY *THE MONSTER OF PELADON*
Tx 23/3/74 - 27/4/74: Six ● ◇ ▲
R 7.7 **Wr** Brian Hayles **Dr** Lennie Mayne **Dgr** Gloria Clayton
The Doctor returns to Peladon fifty years after his first visit and becomes embroiled in an Ice Warrior plot.

ZZZ *PLANET OF THE SPIDERS*
Tx 4/5/74 - 8/6/74: Six ● ◆ ▲
R 9.0 **Wr** Robert Sloman **Dr** Barry Letts **Dgr** Rochelle Selwyn
The spiders of Metebelis Three track down the blue crystal (see The Green Death) and the Doctor's body is irreparably damaged in his final confrontation with the Great One. His regeneration takes place, helped along by a projection (Cho-je) of the Time Lord K'Anpo – the Doctor's past mentor. (K'Anpo subsequently regenerates into Cho-je).

Photo© Topham Picture Source.

In the early Seventies, many television programmes were junked and certain *Doctor Who* stories were lost. Some stories only exist in part and some of Jon Pertwee's adventures, the first to be transmitted in colour, were also victims of this selective junking, with only black and white or United States format copies currently held in the BBC archives. Colour copies that could be broadcast in Britain or released on video are still being sought. All the episodes *Doctor Who* fans are searching for are listed below.

For reasons of space, we have not listed separate episode titles for Hartnell stories. The BBC Archive holds certain Pertwee stories in a variety of formats, such as 525 line, black and white film recordings etc, of which some could be broadcast in the UK in black and white. A word of explanation: The United States (for example) uses a different transmission system to Britain (525 lines, not 625) which means copies held by the BBC previously transmitted there cannot be broadcast in Britain. However, they can be converted to 625 line copies, an operation already in progress (and used for the video release of *Death to the Daleks*).

Copies of stories now held as complete 'Beta SP dubs', have been listed in the main guide; these are suitable for UK transmission and are colour.

All stories from 4A onwards exist in a UK broadcastable format.

WILLIAM HARTNELL Season One: *Marco Polo*, all seven episodes; *The Reign of Terror*, 4, 5. Season Two: *The Crusade*, 1, 2, 4. Season Three: *Galaxy 4*, all four episodes; *Mission to the Unknown*; *The Myth Makers*, all four episodes; *The Daleks' Master Plan*, 1, 2, 3, 4, 6, 7, 8, 9, 11, 12; *The Massacre of St Bartholomew's Eve*, all four episodes; *The Celestial Toymaker*, 1, 2, 3; *The Savages*, all four episodes. Season Four: *The Smugglers*, all four episodes; and *The Tenth Planet*, 4.

PATRICK TROUGHTON Season Four: *The Power of the Daleks*, all six episodes; *The Highlanders*, all four episodes; *The Underwater Menace*, 1, 2, 4; *The Moonbase, 1, 3*; *The Macra Terror*, all four episodes; *The Faceless Ones*, 2, 4, 5, 6; *The Evil of the Daleks*, 1, 3, 4, 5, 6, 7 Season Five: *The Tomb of the Cybermen*, all four episodes; *The Abominable Snowmen*, 1, 3, 4, 5, 6; *The Ice Warriors*, 2, 3; *The Enemy of the World* 1, 2, 4, 5, 6; *The Web of Fear*, 2, 3, 4, 5, 6; *Fury from the Deep*, all six episodes; *The Wheel in Space*, 1, 2, 4, 5. Season Six: *The Invasion*, 1, 4; *The Space Pirates*, 1, 3, 4, 5, 6.

JON PERTWEE (625VT colour recordings sought), Season Seven: *Doctor Who and the Silurians*, all seven episodes; *The Ambassadors of Death*, 2 – 7; *Inferno* all seven episodes. Season Eight: *Terror of the Autons*, all four episodes; *The Mind of Evil*, all six episodes; *The Claws of Axos*, 2, 3; *Colony in Space*, all six episodes; *The Dæmons*, 1, 2, 3, 5. Season Nine: *The Curse of Peladon*, all four episodes; *The Sea Devils*, 1, 2, 3; *The Mutants*, 1, 2; *The Time Monster*, 1-5. Season Ten: *Planet of the Daleks*, 3. Season Eleven: *Invasion (of the Dinosaurs)* 1; *Death to the Daleks*, 1 .

Missing episodes are being recovered all the time, through the painstaking work of the BBC Archive and dedicated members of the general public. Anyone who may have information about such material should contact: the **Archive Selector, BBC Archives, c/o BBC Television Centre, Wood Lane London W12.**

The Fourth Doctor (1974-1981)

Played by Tom Baker

NB All stories from *Robot* exist in the BBC archive in a format suitable for UK transmission.

Season Twelve

Script Editor: Robert Holmes
4A ROBOT
Tx 28/12/74 – 18/1/75: Four ●◇
R 10.2 **Wr** Terrance Dicks **Dr** Christopher Barry **Dgr** Ian Rawnsley
Harry Sullivan (Ian Marter) appears. Benton is promoted from Sergeant to Warrant Officer.

★ *Robot*, the debut for Tom Baker, was also the first serial to be made completely on colour videotape with the location work handled by an Outside Broadcast team and not a film crew. A new title sequence appeared, now featuring the Doctor and the TARDIS.

Producer: Philip Hinchcliffe

4C THE ARK IN SPACE
Tx 25/1/75 – 15/2/75: Four ●◆
R 11.1 **Wr** Robert Holmes **Dr** Rodney Bennett **Dgr** Roger Murray-Leach
4B THE SONTARAN EXPERIMENT
Tx 22/2/75 – 1/3/75: Two ●◇
R 10.7 **Wr** Bob Baker and Dave Martin **Dr** Rodney Bennett **Dgr** Roger Murray-Leach
Recorded totally on OB.

4E GENESIS OF THE DALEKS
Tx 8/3/75 – 12/4/75: Six ●◇
R 9.6 **Wr** Terry Nation **Dr** David Maloney **Dgr** David Spode
First appearance of Davros, creator of the Daleks. The Time Lords persuade the Doctor to attempt to prevent the creation of the Daleks or alter their genetic structure so they evolve as less aggressive creatures.
4D REVENGE OF THE CYBERMEN
Tx 19/4/75 – 10/5/75: Four ●◆
R 9.0 **Wr** Gerry Davis **Dr** Michael E. Briant **Dgr** Roger Murray-Leach ➤

Season Thirteen

◄ **4F** *TERROR OF THE ZYGONS*
Tx 30/8/75 – 20/9/75: Four ● ◆
R 7.5 **Wr** Rober Banks Stewart **Dr** Douglas Camfield **Dgr** Nigel Curzon
Last regular appearance of the Brigadier.

4H *PLANET OF EVIL*
Tx 27/9/75 – 18/10/75: Four ● ◇
R 9.9 **Wr** Louis Marks **Dr** David Maloney **Dgr** Roger Murray-Leach

4G *PYRAMIDS OF MARS*
Tx 25/10/75 – 15/11/75: Four ● ◆
R 10.7 **Wr** Stephen Harris, (Lewis Greifer and Robert Holmes) **Dr** Paddy Russell **Dgr** Christine Ruscoe

4J *THE ANDROID INVASION*
Tx 22/11/75 – 13/12/75: Four ● ◇
R 11.7 **Wr** Terry Nation **Dr** Barry Letts **Dgr** Philip Lindley
Last appearance of Benton and Harry.

4K *THE BRAIN OF MORBIUS*
Tx 3/1/76 – 24/1/76: Four ● ◆
R 9.8 **Wr** Robin Bland (Terrance Dicks) **Dr** Christopher Barry **Dgr** Barry Newbery
First and only appearance of the Sisterhood of Karn, who share their Elixir of Life – an immortality drug – with the Time Lords.

4L *THE SEEDS OF DOOM*
Tx 31/1/76 – 6/3/76: Six ● ◇
R 10.9 **Wr** Rober Banks Stewart **Dr** Douglas Camfield **Dgr** Roger Murray-Leach and Jeremy Bear (Parts One and Two Only)
Last regular UNIT story.

Season Fourteen

4M *THE MASQUE OF MANDRAGORA*
Tx 4/9/76 – 25/9/76: Four ● ◇
R 9.5 **Wr** Louis Marks **Dr** Rodney Bennett **Dgr** Barry Newbery

4N *THE HAND OF FEAR*
Tx 2/10/76 – 23/10/76: Four ● ◇
R 7.0 **Wr** Bob Baker and Dave Martin **Dr** Lennie Mayne **Dgr** Christine Ruscoe
Sarah leaves, the Doctor unable to take her to Gallifrey.

★ *Doctor Who* appeared on radio for the first time on 4th October 1976 when Tom Baker and Elisabeth Sladen played the Doctor and Sarah in an episode of *Exploration Earth* called *The Time Machine.*

4P *THE DEADLY ASSASSIN*
Tx 30/10/76 – 20/11/76: Four ● ◇
R 12.2 **Wr** Robert Holmes **Dr** David Maloney **Dgr** Roger Murray-Leach
The Doctor is pitted against the Master (Peter Pratt) on the Time Lords' own planet, as his arch nemesis seeks to obtain a new cycle of regenerations. The Master is defeated but escapes. First appearance of Borusa – the Doctor's teacher at Academy.

4Q *THE FACE OF EVIL*
Tx 1/1/77 – 22/1/77: Four ● ◇
R 11.2 **Wr** Chris Boucher **Dr** Pennant Roberts **Dgr** Austin Ruddy
Leela (Louise Jameson) of the Sevateem joins the Doctor.

4R *THE ROBOTS OF DEATH*
Tx 29/1/77 – 19/2/77: Four ● ◆
R 12.7 **Wr** Chris Boucher **Dr** Michael E. Briant **Dgr** Kenneth Sharp

4S *THE TALONS OF WENG-CHIANG*
Tx 26/2/77 – 2/4/77: Six ● ◆
R 10.4 **Wr** Robert Holmes **Dr** David Maloney **Dgr** Roger Murray-Leach

Season Fifteen

Producer: Graham Williams
4V *HORROR OF FANG ROCK*
Tx 3/9/77 – 24/9/77: Four ● ◇
R 8.4 **Wr** Terrance Dicks **Dr** Paddy Russell **Dgr** Paul Allen

4T *THE INVISIBLE ENEMY*
Tx 1/10/77 – 22/10/77: Four ● ◇
R 7.9 **Wr** Bob Baker and Dave Martin **Dr** Derrick Goodwin **Dgr** Barry Newbery
K9 Mark I joins, voiced by John Leeson.

4X *IMAGE OF THE FENDAHL*
Tx 29/10/77 – 19/11/77: Four ● ◇
R 7.8 **Wr** Chris Boucher **Dr** George Spenton-Foster **Dgr** Anna Ridley

4W *THE SUN MAKERS*
Tx 26/11/77 – 17/12/77: Four ● ◇
R 8.8 **Wr** Robert Holmes **Dr** Pennant Roberts **Dgr** Tony Snoaden

Script Editor: Anthony Read

4Y *UNDERWORLD*
Tx 7/1/78 – 28/1/78: Four ● ◇
R 9.6 **Wr** Bob Baker and Dave Martin **Dr** Norman Stewart **Dgr** Dick Coles
The Doctor explains the Minyan tragedy that provoked the Time Lords non-interference policy, where Gallifreyan intervention on the

planet Minyos led to that civilisation's self-destruction. The Minyan crew indicate they had many thousands of regenerations in order to complete their quest for the P7E.

4Z *THE INVASION OF TIME*
Tx 4/2/78 – 11/3/78: Six ● ◇
R 10.5 **Wr** David Agnew (Graham Williams and Anthony Read) **Dr** Gerald Blake **Dgr** Barbara Gosnold
The Sontarans, employing the Vardans to assist them, invade Gallifrey. Leela leaves along with K9 Mark I and K9 Mark II is unveiled.

Season Sixteen

(The Key to Time Season)

5A *THE RIBOS OPERATION*
Tx 2/9/78 – 23/9/78: Four ● ◇
R 8.1 **Wr** Robert Holmes **Dr** George Spenton-Foster **Dgr** Ken Ledsham

The Doctor is called upon to collect the six segments of the Key to Time by the White Guardian. The key will be used to restore the cosmic balance. The Doctor and K9 Mark II are joined by the Time Lady, Romanadvoratredlundar (Mary Tamm), better known as Romana.

5B *THE PIRATE PLANET*
Tx 30/9/78 – 21/10/78: Four ○ ◇
R 8.3 **Wr** Douglas Adams **Dr** Pennant Roberts **Dgr** Jon Pusey

5C *THE STONES OF BLOOD*
Tx 28/10/78 – 18/11/78: Four ● ◇
R 8.0 **Wr** David Fisher **Dr** Darrol Blake **Dgr** John Stout

5D *THE ANDROIDS OF TARA*
Tx 25/11/78 – 16/12/78: Four ● ◇
R 9.1 **Wr** David Fisher **Dr** Michael Hayes **Dgr** Valerie Warrender

5E *THE POWER OF KROLL*
Tx 23/12/78 – 13/1/79: Four ● ◇
R 9.4 **Wr** Robert Holmes **Dr** Norman Stewart **Dgr** Don Giles

5F *THE ARMAGEDDON FACTOR*
Tx 20/1/79 – 24/2/79: Six ● ◇
R 8.5 **Wr** Bob Baker and Dave Martin **Dr** Michael Hayes **Dgr** Richard McManan-Smith
Part One: 500th Episode. First appearance of the Black Guardian (played by Valentine Dyall), aided by the Shadow, his servant. In order to elude the Black Guardian when he again scatters the Key to Time across the cosmos, the Doctor fits a Randomiser to the TARDIS console so neither he (nor the Black Guardian) can predict where it will land next.

Season Seventeen

Script Editor: Douglas Adams
5J DESTINY OF THE DALEKS
Tx 1/9/79 – 22/9/79: Four ●◇
R 13.5 **Wr** Terry Nation **Dr** Ken Grieve **Dgr** Ken Ledsham
Romana decides to regenerate (now played by Lalla Ward). The Movellans are introduced, robotic enemies of the Daleks. Davros re-appears.

5H CITY OF DEATH
Tx 29/9/79 – 20/10/79: Four ○◆
R 14.5 **Wr** David Agnew (Douglas Adams and Graham Williams, from an idea by David Fisher) **Dr** Michael Hayes **Dgr** Richard McManan Smith

★ The first story to contain overseas filming was *City of Death* which had material shot on location in Paris, France.

5G THE CREATURE FROM THE PIT
Tx 27/10/79 – 17/11/79: Four ●◇
R 10.0 **Wr** David Fisher **Dr** Christopher Barry **Dgr** Valerie Warrender
K9 now voiced by David Brierley.

5K NIGHTMARE OF EDEN
Tx 24/11/79 – 15/12/79: Four ●◇
R 9.3 **Wr** Bob Baker **Dr** Alan Bromly (and Graham Williams) **Dgr** Roger Cann

5L THE HORNS OF NIMON
Tx 22/12/79 – 12/1/79: Four ●◇
R 9.3 **Wr** Anthony Read **Dr** Kenny McBain **Dgr** Graeme Story

5M SHADA
Untransmitted: *All recorded material held in BBC Archive:* Six ○◇
Wr Douglas Adams **Dr** Pennant Roberts **Dgr** Victor Meredith
Parts used in The Five Doctors.

Season Eighteen

Executive Producer: Barry Letts
Producer: John Nathan-Turner
Script Editor: Christopher H. Bidemead
5N THE LEISURE HIVE
Tx 30/8/80 – 20/9/80: Four ●◇
R 5.1 **Wr** David Fisher **Dr** Lovett Bickford **Dgr** Tom Yardley-Jones
John Leeson returns to voice K9.

5Q MEGLOS
Tx 27/9/80 – 18/10/80: Four ●◇
R 4.6 **Wr** Andrew McCullouch and John Flanagan **Dr** Terence Dudley **Dgr** Philip Lindley

5R FULL CIRCLE
Tx 25/10/80 – 15/11/80: Four ●◇
R 5.2 **Wr** Andrew Smith **Dr** Peter Grimwade **Dgr** Janet Budden
Travelling through a Charged Vacuum Emboitment, the TARDIS is trapped in E-Space. Adric (Matthew Waterhouse) boards the ship.

5P STATE OF DECAY
Tx 22/11/80 – 13/12/80: Four ●◇
R 5.2 **Wr** Terrance Dicks **Dr** Peter Moffatt **Dgr** Christine Ruscoe
The last Great Vampire is killed, the last of a race thought long destroyed during a war against the Time Lords led by Rassilon. The war was said to have been so long and so violent the Time Lords were sickened of violence forever.

5S WARRIORS' GATE
Tx 3/1/81 – 24/1/81: Four ●◇
Tx 7.5 **Wr** Steve Gallagher **Dr** Paul Joyce (and Graeme Harper) **Dgr** Graeme Story
Romana and K9 leave to help the Tharils in E-Space. The TARDIS returns to real space.

5T THE KEEPER OF TRAKEN
Tx 31/1/81 – 21/2/81: Four ●◇
R 6.2 **Wr** Johnny Byrne **Dr** John Black **Dgr** Tony Burrough
The Master (Geoffrey Beevers) re-appears and takes over the body of Tremas to continue his life.

5V LOGOPOLIS
Tx 28/2/81 – 21/3/81: Four ●◇
R 6.7 **Wr** Christopher H. Bidmead **Dr** Peter Grimwade **Dgr** Malcolm Thornton
Seeking to re-configure the TARDIS to enable the chameleon circuits to work again, the Doctor is once again pitted against the Master (Anthony Ainley) and although defeating the evil Time Lord, he is forced into regeneration, assisted by a projection of his new self, the Watcher. Nyssa of Traken (Sarah Sutton) and air hostess Tegan Jovanka (Janet Fielding) join.

K9 AND COMPANY
A Girl's Best Friend

No Executive Producer
Producer: John Nathan Turner
Script Editor: Eric Saward and Antony Root

Tx 28/12/81: One fifty minute episode ●◇
Wr Terence Dudley **Dr** John Black **Dgr** Nigel Johns
Pilot episode for a proposed but unrealised spin-off series featuring Sarah Jane Smith (Elisabeth Sladen) with K9 Mk III (voiced by John Leeson), a present from the Doctor.

The Fifth Doctor (1982–1984)

Played by Peter Davison

Season Nineteen
No Executive Producer from here
Script Editor: Eric Saward

5Z CASTROVALVA
Tx 4/1/82 – 12/1/82: Four ●◇
R 9.9 **Wr** Christopher H. Bidmead **Dr** Fiona Cumming **Dgr** Janet Budden
The new Doctor makes use of the TARDIS Zero Room to assist his regeneration, which is jettisoned along with other parts of the TARDIS to avoid travelling into Event One. The Master is trapped in Castrovalva, a Block Transfer Computation created by Adric, when it vanishes.

★ *Castrovalva* was not only the first Peter Davison serial, but Part One was the first episode to feature a pre-credit sequence — coming before a new opening titles. It was also the first time a first run episode on BBC1 had gone out on a day rather than a Saturday, starting a twice-weekly schedule.

Script Editor: Antony Root

5W FOUR TO DOOMSDAY
Tx 18/1/82 – 26/1/82: Four ●◇
R 9.0 **Wr** Terence Dudley **Dr** John Black **Dgr** Tony Burrough

Script Editor: Eric Saward

5Y KINDA
Tx 1/2/82 – 9/2/82: Four
R 9.0 **Wr** Christopher Bailey **Dr** Peter Grimwade **Dgr** Malcolm Thornton
First appearance of the Mara.

Script Editor: Antony Root

5X THE VISITATION
Tx 15/2/82 – 23/2/82: Four ●◇
R 9.8 **Wr** Eric Saward **Dr** Peter Moffatt **Dgr** Ken Starkey
The Doctor inadvertently starts the 1666 Great Fire of London when he destroys the alien Terileptil leader. The Doctor's sonic screwdriver is destroyed.

◄ *Script Editor: Eric Saward*

6A *BLACK ORCHID*
Tx 1/3/82 – 2/3/82: Two ● ◇
R 9.2 **Wr** Terence Dudley **Dr** Ron Jones **Dgr** Tony Burrough

Script Editor: Antony Root

6B *EARTHSHOCK*
Tx 8/3/82 – 16/3/82: Four ● ◇
R 9.3 **Wr** Eric Saward **Dr** Peter Grimwade
Dgr Bernard Lloyd-Jones
Adric foils a Cyberman plot to destroy Twenty-Sixth century Earth by re-routing a space freighter through a time spiral. It crashes on Earth sixty-five million years in the past, killing the Doctor's young companion and causing the dinosaurs' extinction.

Script Editor: Eric Saward

6C *TIME-FLIGHT*
Tx 22/3/82 – 30/3/82: Four ● ◇
R 9.0 **Wr** Peter Grimwade **Dr** Ron Jones **Dgr** Richard McManan-Smith
The Doctor again defeats the Master but Tegan is left on Twentieth-Century Earth.

Season Twenty
6E *ARC OF INFINITY*
Tx 3/1/83 – 12/1/83: Four ● ◇
R 7.2 **Wr** Johnny Byrne **Dr** Ron Jones **Dgr** Marjorie Pratt
Tegan rejoins and Omega returns, defeated by the Doctor using a matter convertor.
6D *SNAKEDANCE*
Tx 18/1/83 – 26/1/83: Four ● ◇
R 7.1 **Wr** Christopher Bailey **Dr** Fiona Cumming **Dgr** Jan Spoczynski
Second Mara story.

6F *MAWDRYN UNDEAD*
Tx 1/2/83 – 9/2/83: Four ● ◇
R 7.3 **Wr** Peter Grimwade **Dr** Peter Moffatt **Dgr** Stephen Scott

40

Turlough (Mark Strickson) joins, an agent of the Black Guardian ordered to kill the Doctor. Lethbridge-Stewart appears, now a school teacher.

6G *TERMINUS*
Tx 15/2/83 – 23/2/83: Four ● ◇
R 7.1 **Wr** Steve Gallagher **Dr** Mary Ridge **Dgr** Dick Coles
Nyssa leaves.

6H *ENLIGHTENMENT*
Tx 1/3/83 – 9/3/83: Four ● ◇
R 6.8 **Wr** Barbara Clegg **Dr** Fiona Cumming **Dgr** Colin Green
The Black Guardian is defeated and Turlough is freed from his power.
6J *THE KING'S DEMONS*
Tx 15/3/83 – 16/3/83: Two ● ◇
R 6.5 **Wr** Terence Dudley **Dr** Tony Virgo **Dgr** Ken Ledsham
Kamelion (voiced by Gerald Flood) joins the Doctor's crew when the Master makes another appearance, plotting to twist Earth history and ensure the Magna Carta is not signed.

6K *THE FIVE DOCTORS*
Tx 25/11/83 – (23/11/83, USA): One ● ◆
(Ninety Minute Special)
R 7.7 **Wr** Terrance Dicks **Dr** Peter Moffatt (and John Nathan-Turner) **Dgr** Malcolm Thornton
The Doctors (the First Doctor played by Richard Hurndall) are summoned to the Death Zone on Gallifrey, part of a plot conceived by Lord President Borusa to achieve immortality. A Dalek, the Cybermen and the Master are among those drawn into the Game of Rassilon before Borusa is defeated – but not in a way he expects.

THE DOCTOR'S TOP TWENTY
The chart below records the Doctor's most popular stories in Britain, based on the average ratings the story acheived, recorded in millions. In brackets is listed the Doctor who starred:

1	City of Death (Tom Baker)	14.50m˙
2	Pyramids of Mars – Edited Repeat (Tom Baker)	13.70m
3	Destiny of the Daleks (Tom Baker)	13.48m˙
4	The Robots of Death (Tom Baker)	12.72m
5	The Web Planet (William Hartnell)	12.50m
6	The Rescue (William Hartnell)	12.50m
7	The Deadly Assassin (Tom Baker)	12.18m
8	The Dalek Invasion of Earth (William Hartnell)	11.90m
9	The Android Invasion (Tom Baker)	11.68m
10	The Romans (William Hartnell)	11.62m
11	The Face of Evil (Tom Baker)	11.20m
12	The Ark in Space (Tom Baker)	11.10m
13	The Hand of Fear (Tom Baker)	10.95m
14	The Seeds of Doom (Tom Baker)	10.60m
15	The Brain of Morbius – Edited Repeat (Tom Baker)	10.90m
16	The Sontaran Experiment (Tom Baker)	11.93m
17	The Dæmons – Edited Repeat (Jon Pertwee)	10.53m
18	The Invasion of Time (Tom Baker)	10.52m
19	The Green Death – Edited Repeat (Jon Pertwee)	10.45m
20	The Talons of Weng-Chiang (Tom Baker)	10.35m

*An ITV strike increased viewing figures for most BBC programmes when these stories were first broadcast.

Fifth Doctor Peter Davison's highest placing in a chart of all *Who* stories is at Number 25 with his debut story *Castrovalva* with Patrick Troughton's highest rated story being *The Moonbase*, a Cyberman story joint equal at the Number 64 position with William Hartnell's *The Celestial Toymaker*. As viewing habits change (although audience appreciation of the programme remains generally high throughout the series twenty–eight years) Colin Baker's highest placing is with *Attack of the Cybermen* at Number 72. The Seventh Doctor, his adventures placed against *Coronation Street*, a long running and very popular soap opera, enters the chart at Number 134 with the twenty-fifth anniversary story, *Silver Nemesis*.
Source: BARB

Season Twenty-One

6L *WARRIORS OF THE DEEP*
Tx 5/1/84 – 13/1/84: Four ● ◇
R 7.2 **Wr** Johnny Byrne **Dr** Penant Roberts
Dgr Tony Burrough
The Sea Devils and the Silurians unite in an attempt to provoke two human power blocs into nuclear war.

6M *THE AWAKENING*
Tx 19/1/84 – 20/1/84: Two ● ◇
R 7.2 **Wr** Eric Pringle **Dr** Michael Owen Morris **Dgr** Barry Newbery

6N *FRONTIOS*
Tx 26/1/84 – 3/2/84: Four ● ◇
R 6.8 **Wr** Christopher H. Bidmead **Dr** Ron Jones **Dgr** David Buckingham

6P *RESURRECTION OF THE DALEKS*
Tx 8/2/84 – 15/2/84: Two (Forty-five and fifty minute episodes) ◯ ◇
R 7.6 **Wr** Eric Saward **Dr** Matthew Robinson **Dgr** John Anderson
Tegan leaves, disgusted by the violence of the Doctor's adventures. First appearance of Lytton (played by Maurice Colbourne).

6Q *PLANET OF FIRE*
Tx 23/2/84 – 2/3/84: Four ● ◇
R 7.0 **Wr** Peter Grimwade **Dr** Fiona Cumming **Dgr** Malcolm Thornton
Turlough leaves, Peri (Perpugilliam) Brown joins. Kamelion is destroyed.

6R *THE CAVES OF ANDROZANI*
Tx 8/3/84 – 16/3/84: Four ● ◇
R 7.3 **Wr** Robert Holmes **Dr** Graeme Harper **Dgr** John Hurst
Poisoned by raw Spectrox on Androzani Minor, the Doctor regenerates. Colin Baker's first appearance.

The Sixth Doctor (1984–1986)

Played by Colin Baker
6S *THE TWIN DILEMMA*
Tx 22/3/84 – 30/3/84: Four ● ◇
R 7.1 **Wr** Anthony Steven **Dr** Peter Moffatt **Dgr** Valerie Warender
Behaving erratically, the Doctor attacks Peri and then decides to become a hermit

before he becomes embroiled in a plot conceived by the renegade Time Lord, Azmael.

Season Twenty-Two

(Episodes this season: Forty-five minutes each)
6T *ATTACK OF THE CYBERMEN*
Tx 5/1/85 – 12/1/85: Two ● ◇
R 8.0 **Wr** Paula Moore **Dr** Matthew Robinson **Dgr** Marjorie Pratt
Last appearance of Lytton. The Doctor attempts to repair the TARDIS' chameleon circuit with bizarre results.

6V *VENGEANCE ON VAROS*
Tx 19/1/85 – 26/1/85: Two
R 7.1 **Wr** Philip Martin **Dr** Ron Jones **Dgr** Tony Soaden
First appearance of Sil (played by Nabil Shaban).

6X *THE MARK OF THE RANI*
Tx 2/2/85 – 9/2/85: Two ● ◇
R 7.0 **Wr** Pip and Jane Baker **Dr** Sarah Hellings **Dgr** Paul Trerise
First appearance of the Rani (played by Kate O'Mara), a female renegade Time Lord.

6W *THE TWO DOCTORS*
Tx 16/2/85 – 2/3/85: Three ● ◇
R 6.5 **Wr** Robert Holmes **Dr** Peter Moffatt **Dgr** Tony Burrough
The Second and Sixth Doctors are embroiled in a plot by the Sontarans to gain the secrets of time travel technology. The Second Doctor's TARDIS is under the control of the Time Lords, for reasons unexplained.

6Y *TIMELASH*
Tx 9/3/85 – 16/3/85: Two ● ◇
R 7.0 **Wr** Glen McCoy **Dr** Pennant Roberts **Dgr** Bob Cove

6Z *REVELATION OF THE DALEKS*
Tx 23/3/85 – 30/3/85: Two ◯ ◇
R 7.6 **Wr** Eric Saward **Dr** Graeme Harper **Dgr** Alan Spalding
Davros re-appears but is captured by the Imperial Daleks as he tries to create a new, more aggressive race of Daleks.

THE MISSING SEASON TWENTY-THREE
Several stories were commissioned for Season Twenty-Three before the BBC delayed production of *Doctor Who* (for a variety of reasons) in February 1985. Scripts under consideration included the return of the Autons and the Rani, with submissions from Robert Holmes and Christopher H. Bidemead in addition to those now novelised as Target novels, featuring the Sixth Doctor and Peri, which are:

THE NIGHTMAIR FAIR
Wr Graham Williams
The Doctor is pitted against the Celestial Toymaker once more against the backdrop of a Blackpool Fun Fair.

THE ULTIMATE EVIL
Wr. Wally K. Daly
The TARDIS working perfectly, the Doctor plans a holiday in Tranquela, a peaceful country. His visit coincides with that of an unscrupulous arms dealer – the Machiavellan Dwarf Mordant.

MISSION TO MAGNUS
Wr Philip Martin
The Ice Warriors return alongside the villainous Sil in attempt to freeze an entire world and wipe out most of its population.

Season Twenty-Three

Note: the following four stories were all broadcast as *The Trial of a Time Lord*, comprising 14 episodes.

7A *PARTS 1–4*
(Book Title: *The Mysterious Planet*)
Tx 6/9/86 – 27/9/86: Four ● ◇
R 4.4 **Wr** Robert Holmes **Dr** Nick Mallett **Dgr** John Anderson
The Doctor is called to trial, prosecuted for various alleged crimes by the mysterious Valeyard (played by Michael Jayston). First appearance of the mercenary, Glitz (played by Tony Selby).

7B *PARTS 5–8*
(Book Title: *Mindwarp*)
Tx 4/10/86 – 25/10/86: Four ● ◇
R 4.9 **Wr** Philip Martin **Dr** Ron Jones **Dgr** Andrew Howe-Davis
Peri apparently dies (but it is revealed in 7C that this was a lie constructed by the Valeyard).

No Script Editor credited

7C *PARTS 9–12*
(Book Title: *Terror of the Vervoids*)
Tx 1/11/86 – 22/11/86: Four ● ◇
R 5.1 **Wr** Pip and Jane Baker **Dr** Chris Clough **Dgr** Dinah Walker
Mel (Bonnie Langford) joins.

Script Editor: Eric Saward (Part 13 only) ➤

◄ **7C** *PARTS 13–14*
(Book Title: *The Ultimate Foe*)
Tx 29/11/86 – 6/12/86: Two ● ◇
R 5.0 **Wr** Robert Holmes (Part Thirteen)
and Pip and Jane Baker (Part Fourteen) **Dr**
Chris Clough **Dgr** Michael Trevor
*Last adventure to feature Colin Baker as the
Sixth Doctor to date. The Valeyard is
revealed as an amalgamation of the
Doctor's darker side, between his twelfth
and final regeneration. The Doctor wrecks
the Valeyard's plans but the villain seems to
escape as the Keeper of the Matrix, with
Gallifrey in disarray.*

The Seventh Doctor (1987 – ?)

Played by Sylvester McCoy

Season Twenty- Four
Script Editor: Andrew Cartmel

7D *TIME AND THE RANI*
Tx 7/9/87 – 28/9/87: Four ● ◇
R 4.6 **Wr** Pip and Jane Baker **Dr** Andrew
Morgan **Dgr** Geoff Powell
*The Seventh Doctor makes his first
appearance. This latest regeneration is
brought on by temporal buffeting of his
TARDIS, caused by the Rani, who is trying
to create a Time Manipulator through the
use of Strange Matter.*

7E *PARADISE TOWERS*
Tx 5/10/87 – 26/10/87: Four ● ◇
R 4.9 **Wr** Stephen Wyatt **Dr** Nicholas
Mallett **Dgr** Martin Collins

7F *DELTA AND THE BANNERMEN*
Tx 2/11/87 – 16/11/87: Three ● ◇
R 5.3 **Wr** Malcolm Kohll **Dr** Chris Clough
Dgr John Asbridge

★ *Remembrance of the Daleks* **Part
One was the first episode to be
transmitted with a Nicam stereo
soundtrack.**

7G *DRAGONFIRE*
Tx 23/11/87 – 7/12/87: Three ● ◇
R 5.1 **Wr** Ian Briggs **Dr** Chris Clough **Dgr**
John Asbridge
*Mel leaves, Ace (Sophie Aldred) joins, as
the evil Kane is defeated by the passage of
Time itself on Iceworld.*

Season Twenty-Five
7H *REMEMBRANCE OF THE DALEKS*
Tx 5/10/88 – 26/10/88: Four ● ◇
R 5.4 **Wr** Ben Aaronvitch **Dr** Andrew
Morgan **Dgr** Martin Collins
*The Doctor uses the Hand of Omega, a
Time Lord weapon of incredible power, to
trick Davros (now Emperor of the Daleks)
himself into destroying the Daleks' home
planet, Skaro.*

7L *THE HAPPINESS PATROL*
Tx 2/11/88 – 16/11/88: Three ● ◇
R 5.1 **Wr** Graeme Curry **Dr** Chris Clough
Dgr John Asbridge

FAMOUS MONSTERS

Doctor Who's most popular foes, based
on polls in *Doctor Who Magazine*, are as
follows (together with their first
appearance):

The Daleks (*The Daleks*)
The Cybermen (*The Tenth Planet*)
The Ice Warriors (*The Ice Warriors*)
The Zygons (*Terror of the Zygons*)
The Sontarans (*The Time Warrior*)
The Autons (*Spearhead from Space*)
The Yeti (*The Abominable Snowmen*)
The Sea Devils (*The Sea Devils*)

Sil (*Vengeance on Varos*)
The Krynoids (*The Seeds of Doom*)

7K *SILVER NEMESIS*
Tx 23/11/88 – 7/11/88: Three ● ◇
R 5.5 **Wr** Kevin Clarke **Dr** Chris Clough **Dgr**
John Asbridge
*Twenty-Fifth anniversary story. The
Cybermen return in an attempt to gain the
validium in a crashed asteroid on Earth,
living metal created by Rassilon that was
once Gallifrey's ultimate defence. They are
not alone in this quest and the mad, evil
Lady Peinforte hints at the Doctor's darker
origins compared with those already
revealed in past adventures. . .*

7J *THE GREATEST SHOW IN THE GALAXY*
Tx 14/12/88 – 4/1/89: Four ● ◇
R 5.4 **Wr** Stephen Wyatt **Dr** Alan Wareing
Dgr David Laskey

Season Twenty-Six

7N *BATTLEFIELD*
Tx 6/9/89 – 27/9/89: Four ○ ◇
R 3.6 **Wr** Ben Aaronvitch **Dr** Michael
Kerrigan **Dgr** Martin Collins
*UNIT calls Lethbridge-Stewart out of
retirement.*

7Q *GHOST LIGHT*
Tx 4/10/89 – 18/10/89: Three ● ◇
R 4.0 **Wr** Marc Platt **Dr** Alan Wareing **Dgr**
Nick Somerville

7M *THE CURSE OF FENRIC*
Tx 25/10/89 – 15/11/89: Four ● ◆
(Extended version)
R 4.1 **Wr** Ian Briggs **Dr** Nicholas Mallett **Dgr**
David Laskey
*1943: as the Haemovores attack a navy
base, the Doctor and Ace are pitted against
Fenric, a menace imprisoned by the Time
Lord over seventeen centuries previously,
who engineered Ace's meeting with the
Doctor on Iceworld.*

7P *SURVIVAL*
Tx 22/11/89 – 6/12/89: Three ● ◇
R 4.9 **Wr** Rona Munro **Dr** Alan Wareing **Dgr**
Nick Somerville
*The Master returns, aided by a cat-like
dimension spanning race and the Doctor
and Ace are embroiled in a battle against
the Time Lord, set in both Perivale on Earth
and a dying alien planet.*

THE CONTINUING ADVENTURES. . .

Since the end of Season Twenty-Six,
there's been a bit of a delay before the
Doctor's adventures continue on television.
However, new stories have continued in
comic strip and novel form since *Survival*,
the last televised story to date. Although
never acknowledged as part of the series'
continuity, these are as follows, listed in
order of their taking place in the Seventh
Doctor's life:

Fellow Travellers (Strip) by Andrew Cartmel
The Mark of Mandragora (Strip) by Dan
Abnett
(Featuring the return of the Mandragora
Helix, last seen in *The Masque of
Mandragora*)
Party Animals (Strip) by Gary Russell
The Chameleon Factor (Strip) By Paul
Cornell
Under Pressure (Strip) by Dan Abnett
The Good Soldier (Strip) by Andrew
Cartmel
(Featuring the Cybermen)
Genesys (Novel) by John Peel
Exodus (Novel) by Terrance Dicks
Apocalypse (Novel) by Nigel Robinson
Revelation (Novel) by Paul Cornell

The Deal

Mel had been looking for the Doctor for some considerable time when she finally gave way to temptation and chose to ignore the handwritten sign bearing the legend "Go away! — Extreme Danger" on a door she hadn't come across before. It was down a corridor, which looked remarkably similar to every other corridor in the TARDIS. It was also next door to the "Gymnasium", whose interior was unsurprisingly devoid of anything remotely designed to stimulate the heart-rate — unless you lived in morbid fear of a half-strung tennis racket, a pair of cricket trousers and a strange twisted wooden object with a long-deflated balloon at one end and a spike at the other, upon whose purpose Mel chose not to speculate.

Having defied the interdiction and thrown open the door, Mel saw the Doctor flicking through a mammoth leather bound volume which he had presumably plucked from one of the many shelves in what was very obviously the TARDIS Library.

"Can't you read?" he threw over his shoulder, by way of greeting. Before, however, she could confirm that she did indeed possess that very useful skill, which was why she just might have appreciated knowing about the Library — he continued — "Anyway no time to waste, follow me!" He plucked his awful jacket off the back of a chair and strode off towards the TARDIS' console room muttering to himself. Mel set off after him asking "What's so urgent, and what's that huge book? And where are we going now?"

"Everything, my address book and Vertipax" he replied, as he arrived at the Console and threw many switches in quick succession (at least half of which Mel was convinced did nothing useful other than impress those susceptible to such flamboyance).

When, a short time later, they emerged from the TARDIS, Mel saw that they had materialised outside what the manufacturers of tin shacks would be deeply offended to have credited as one of their products. "Dilapidated" was as accurate a description of this structure as "large-ish" would be of the Palace of Versailles. Before Mel could express her forebodings which were principally stimulated by her very keen sense of smell, the Doctor had thrown open (and then away) the flimsy door and entered. Inside, a predominantly green, partially humaniform and disturbingly moist creature was introduced to Mel as "my old friend, Mosca Ragazzo". The Doctor produced a pile of photographs, which Mel glimpsed only briefly as the creature scrutinised them (if waving half a dozen antennae in the general direction of something could be defined as scrutinising).

Then Mosca handed (or "pseudopoded") the Doctor a small shiny object.

They regained the fresh air and witnessed the bizarre sight of a score of small driverless tractors loading packing cases into the limitless inner reaches of the TARDIS, apparently in exchange for the small shiny object. Mel's insistent queries were repeatedly ignored or impatiently dismissed by the Doctor.

It was only after the time-space machine dematerialised and left Vertipax, that the Doctor suddenly and disarmingly benignly turned to Mel and said, "Well, that was a good day's work, wouldn't you say?"

"I'm sure I might say that ➤

43

Doctor, if I knew what has been going on!" protested Mel to the Doctor's back as he strode off back to the Library.

"Well, what would you like to know? All you have to do is ask you know. I may have many remarkable talents but mind-reading isn't one of them." Mel knew better than to argue.

"Well", she said, "let's start with an explanation of what we've been doing since I found you in here with your 'address book'."

"I'll have to take you back a little earlier than that," replied the Doctor. "Long before the Time Lords looked outward from Galli-frey, a race called the Verval-loochenen set up Vertipax to monitor what they saw as the threat of pollution in the Universe. Planetary systems would be checked every three or four thousand years, and any pollution threatening the continued exist-ence of a planet would be eradicated."

"We could do with them on Earth," interrupted Mel.

"Mmmm, yes, well I'll be coming to that," said the Doctor. "You remember those trips we made to Earth recently..."

"How could I forget landing twenty or thirty times in quick succession and waiting while you nipped outside with a vacuum cleaner and, as usual, wouldn't tell me why?"

"I was only protecting you, Mel. Anyway ... I was just planting a little circumstantial evidence to help my friend Mosca Ragazzo. I'm afraid that the noble intentions of the Vervalloochenen have become somewhat diluted over the mille-nia and their successors have sub-contracted what they consider to be a worthwhile but somewhat onerous task.

"A long way down the subcon-tracting chain is Mosca, who calls himself an entrepreneur, though others might have a less flattering description. He was naturally delighted when I offered to go to Earth and tidy up a little pollution problem on his behalf – especially as he could make a sizeable profit on the deal."

Mel interrupted "But what on Earth were you doing with the vacuum cleaner, Doctor?"

"Atmosphere redistribution generators" corrected the Doctor, "I was just re-arranging local topography, Mel, A few crops here and there flattened into neat little circles to prove to Mosca's con-tractors that his ships had been there and done the job. The local inhabitants would have been dis-missed as fruit cases."

"Nut" corrected Mel "or cake".

"Don't you ever think of any-thing but food," the Doctor snapped, "Please don't interrupt! Anyway, Mosca was very pleased with the "evidence" of his job well done and paid up. Unfortunately, he wouldn't have trusted me if I had offered to fill in for him for nothing, but he couldn't resist the opportunity of bettering me on a deal. Hence the packages in the store room."

"What's in them Doctor?"

"These!" he replied producing from his pocket the largest, stickiest chocolate bar Mel had ever seen. "They're a powerful antidote to carrots!" He grinned.

But Mel had not finished. "Aside from your hopeless eating habits, Doctor, I am appalled that you, of all people should be so irresponsi-ble! You should have done every-thing possible to help clear pollu-tion on Earth – I can't *believe* that you could let the people of Earth down so badly for a few chocolate bars. You have always professed to have a special fondness for them!"

"What? Chocolate bars?" smirked the Doctor innocently.

"No! The people of Earth!" shouted Mel.

"I have, my dear. You don't quite understand. In the eyes of the Vervalloochenen agency, it is the people of Earth who *are* the pollution! At least you now have another few thousand years."

He resisted the temptation to pop a chocolate bar into her wide open mouth.

Colin Baker

UNDER PRESSURE

PART 2.

COME ON, CLEAR THIS DECK! MOVE IT!

"THE ENORMITY OF THE SITUATION WAS JUST DAWNING ON ME WHEN THINGS ALL BECAME RATHER WORSE..."

COME ON, MOVE IT, YOU RABBLE! WE HAVE TO SEAL THIS SECTION OFF.

WHAT WAS IT? WHAT HIT US?

I DON'T KNOW. JUST MOVE IT-EH?

SSSHHH

OH MY...

NO! HELP ME! NO! NO!

SHRAKK!

"I WAS STILL TOO BUSY TRYING TO REMEMBER WHAT I WAS MEANT TO SAY AND DO..."

BLAST IT! NO, I COULDN'T HAVE DONE THAT, I...

MISTER HARDY! I'VE GOT REPORTS OF AN ATTACK IN THE ENGINE ROOM... THEY'RE TALKING ABOUT **MONSTERS** SIR!

WHAT?

IT'S STARTED...

HARDY! GET YOUR MEN TO TRY AND SEAL OFF THE ENGINE ROOM!

THOUGH THE SEA DEVILS WILL CUT THROUGH SOON ENOUGH...

GIVE ME THAT... JUTLAND, THIS IS TEMPEST. I WANT TO SPEAK TO THE DOCTOR, OVER.

DOCTOR HERE. WHO'S THIS?

NO TIME TO EXPLAIN. THE SEA DEVILS HAVE BEGUN THEIR ATTACK. WHEN THEY'VE GOT CONTROL OF THE ENGINE ROOM IN FIVE MINUTES TIME, THEY'LL BEGIN TO MELTDOWN THE REACTORS...

HOW DO YOU KNOW IT'LL TAKE FIVE MINUTES? SURELY WE HAVE LONGER...

OOPS...

THAT WAS JUST A GUESS! LISTEN TO ME... ARE YOU PICKING UP THE SEA DEVILS' TRANSMISSIONS?

NO. I'LL TRY AND—

BOOST THE SIGNAL THROUGH EIGHT EIGHTY CYCLES!

... JUST WHAT I WAS ABOUT TO DO...

THESE SEA DEVIL THINGS HAVE BROKEN INTO THE MAIN ENGINE ROOM. WE CAN'T CONTAIN THEM.

CARRY ON, MISTER HARDY. I'M NEARLY THERE...

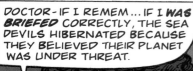

DOCTOR - IF I REMEM... IF I *WAS BRIEFED* CORRECTLY, THE SEA DEVILS HIBERNATED BECAUSE THEY BELIEVED THEIR PLANET WAS UNDER THREAT.

YOUR INFORMATION IS EXCELLENT. I'D LIKE TO DISCUSS THIS FURTHER WITH YOU WHEN THIS IS ALL OVER...

WE'LL WORRY ABOUT THAT LATER, DOCTOR. WOULD I BE RIGHT IN SAYING THEIR RECENT REVIVAL AND AGGRESSIVE URGES ARE DUE TO THEM UNDERSTANDING THIS IS NO LONGER THE CASE...

... AND THEREFORE WISHING TO EXTERMINATE THE UPSTART MAMMAL...

... THAT HAS USURPED THEIR SUPERIORITY ON EARTH?

PERFECTLY CORRECT. WHY?

BECAUSE THEN WE HAVE TO LIE TO THEM...

WHAT DID YOU MEAN, *LIE?* WHAT ARE YOU DOING?

SSHH, HARDY! THE ONLY WAY OF THWART-ING THE SEA DEVILS' ATTACK ON THIS CRAFT IS TO *RE-INFORM* THEM OF THE SITUATION.

BUT AFTER THE BUSINESS AT THE RIG, WE *WANTED* TO FIND THEM, TO MAKE CONTACT...

YOU'VE DONE NOTHING BUT WAKE THEM UP. THIS WAS A FOOL'S ERRAND THAT SHOULD NEVER HAVE TAKEN PLACE...

... I'M SURPRISED I EVER THOUGHT OF IT, REALLY.

HELLO, TEMPEST. I'VE DRAFTED *OUR REPLY.* THANKS FOR YOUR INPUT. I ONLY HOPE IT WORKS.

TRANSMITTING IT DOWN TO YOU NOW. STAND BY TO LOAD IT A-BOARD YOUR ACOUSTIC BEACON.

GO AHEAD, DOCTOR...

EXCELLENT. *EXCELLENT!*

COULDN'T HAVE DONE IT WITHOUT MY LEXICAL CONSTRUCTIONS THOUGH...

THEY'RE NEARLY HERE, DOCTOR!

FORGET THEM. IS THE ACOUSTIC TORPEDO IN THE TUBES?

YES SIR...

THE INFORMATION'S LOADED. FIRE WHEN READY.

FIRE!

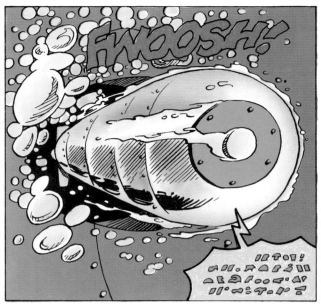

FWOOSH!

"THE TORPEDO'S BROADCASTING, DOCTOR. BUT WHAT'S IT SAYING TO THEM?"

"A GREAT LIE, HARDY. IT'S TELLING THEM THAT THEIR WORLD IS STILL UNDER THREAT AND THAT THEY MUST RETURN TO THEIR DEEP SLEEP IN ORDER TO SURVIVE."

"WILL IT WORK?"

"WHO KNOWS?"

"AND IF IT DOESN'T?"

"THAT'S SIMPLE..."

"...KISMET, HARDY."

"DOCTOR! REPORTS FROM ALL LEVELS. THEY'RE GOING BACK! THEY'RE RETREATING!"

BACK TO SLEEP... I MUST GO NOW.

GO?

GO... BELOW ...TO CHECK ON THINGS, HARDY.

TEMPEST. TEMPEST! COME IN. THIS IS THE DOCTOR.

FIRST OFFICER HARDY RESPONDING. DANGER AVERTED. THANKS TO THE DOCTOR, WE'RE SAFE.

NICE OF YOU TO SAY SO, HARDY. WE'VE GOT VISUAL BACK ON LINE. I WANT TO TALK TO YOUR SCIENTIFIC ADVISOR. PUT HIM ON THE SCREEN.

DOCTOR! WAIT! I'VE GOT VISUAL LINK COMING THROUGH...

REALLY HARDY. I MUST BE OFF.

BESIDES, I HATE APPEARING IN PERSONS.

DOCTOR... WHO IS THAT?

I DON'T KNOW, JO...

...I'VE NEVER SEEN HIM BEFORE IN MY LIFE.

TALKING TO YOURSELF, EH?

IT HAPPENS ONCE IN A WHILE.

KNOW THYSELF, ACE... BUT NOT TOO WELL...

EVEN WHEN YOU'RE CAUGHT BETWEEN THE DEVIL AND THE DEEP BLUE SEA.

...DRINK AND THE DEVIL HAD DONE FOR THE REST... YO HO HO AND A BOTTLE OF RUM...

Behind the Scenes

Photo © Tomek Bork.

Former *Doctor Who* producer John Nathan-Turner describes the headaches and happier moments in making a new adventure for the errant Time Lord . . .

With every *Doctor Who* story, there are problems. With every television programme, there are problems. The main problem, it seems to me, is remembering the problems when you're asked to write an article about the problems of a project, two years after the problems were dealt with. The problems remain relatively clear, but the order of events gets a little cloudy!

Let us start with the delivery of the script of *Wolf-time*, as its working title was known, written by Ian Briggs. It was a first-class script, about which my Script Editor, Andrew Cartmel, and I had few reservations, apart from its epic nature and its title. It was an expensive project from the start, and was the second to be recorded for the Twenty-Sixth Season, involving the usual mix of outside Broadcast and Studio facilities.

I had originally offered the project to Michael Kerrigan, a Director new to *Doctor Who*, who had accepted the seventeen-week contract before the script was delivered. Just as well. The first story which was planned to be recorded featured the return of the Brigadier (Nicholas Courtney). As many of you will know, Nicholas and I have become close friends over the years and regularly confide in one another.

Nicholas had been short-listed for a role in the play, *M. Butterfly*, with Anthony Hopkins . . . a short run out-of-town to be followed by a West-End transfer. At the time, Nicholas had already agreed to return to *Doctor Who* for one story, (*Battlefield*), but contracts were not signed. Nicholas couldn't decide whether to do *M. Butterfly*, if the offer materialised, or see if he got it and turn it down (he didn't like the script) or . . . or . . . or. So I made the situation a little easier. I decided to switch the recording of the first two stories, so that, if Nicholas won the role and accepted it, *Battlefield* would be recorded after *M. Butterfly* had opened in the West End. The only problem this plan produced was how Nicholas could be filming in the Lake District during the day (excluding two matinee days) and commute to London's West End.

With the help of Nicholas' agent, we asked the theatre management, if, all things being equal, Mr Courtney might be granted a few nights off, once the show had premiered in London. The answer was in the negative, so ideas of moving the Legend of King Arthur nearer the Ballspond Road started to surface.

53

The finishing touches to the *Wolftime* script were made. Nicholas Mallett joined the production with his team, to direct story number one and loved the script with its new title *The Wolves of Fenric*. Production Manager, Ian Fraser, set off to find a war-time army camp, as near to London as possible for financial reasons and Nicholas Courtney won the role in *M.Butterfly*. Surprisingly, perhaps, he then turned it down. Early expeditions to the Ballspond Road were put down to experience and King Arthur was re-routed to the Lake District.

During the first few weeks of a Director's engagement, he or she is involved with many diverse activities: casting, of course, script conferences with editor, writer and producer, and initial design meetings. The designers of settings, make-up, costume, visual effects etc will each have a meeting with the director, his production team and, whenever possible, the producer, to discuss the 'look' of the story in general, and the individual area of the designer's involvement, in particular.

Before Nicholas joined the show as Director, the visual effects designer had come up with an early design and model for the head of the Haemovores, as his previous project had completed ahead of

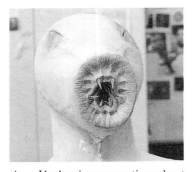

time. I had major reservations about the design, as it resembled, in part, something we'd done before and it didn't, for me anyway, indicate the evolution of the hideous beings. Nicholas decided he wanted costume designer, Ken Trew, to design the monsters, particularly as visual effects had an enormous involvement to cope with already.

Run for it! Ace and the Doctor escape Commander Millington's booby trap. Sylvester's comment: "Hmm, that was a good one, eh, Ace?" Photos © Tomek Bork.

WHO DOES WHAT?

After a 'mulling over' period, the 'Who-Does-What' meeting took place. Just as it sounds, virtually everyone who gets a TV credit, except the artists, foregathers to discuss precisely how everything in the script, and everything the director is adding as part of his 'action', will be achieved. This usually takes a whole day. Some things are put on hold for later discussion, but most methods are decided. It is usually after this meeting that all the designers scream for more money. June Collins, the Production Associate and I and the Director, and if it substantially affects the script, the editor will discuss what can be cut in visual terms and June hands over revised budgets, which the designers will, hopefully, adhere to.

Every Associate keeps what Producers call 'Knicker-elastic' money in reserve for emergencies. In the case of *Fenric*, we needed it!

Meanwhile Ian Fraser continued to scour the nearby countryside for the main location . . . the army camp. Once that was found, the cottage, church, etc could hopefully be found nearby. Our plan was to film 'AWAY' only for the beach and sea sequences. Ian announced after helpful liaison with the Ministry of Defence that the camp could not be found within twenty-five miles of Ealing – the basis of 'HOME' filming. (I must add, at this point, that although we record an Outside Broadcast on videotape, the term 'filming' is still often used . . . probably because "O.B.-ing" doesn't have quite the same ring to it!)

June and I agreed to find some knicker-elastic money to permit the entire location shoot to be filmed away from 'Home'. As the army camp, still unfound, and the shore had to be away, it seemed pointless to split the shooting schedule with travel, which still had to be paid for. Little did we know!

Nicholas continued with splendid improvisation auditions, as many of the parts were vitally important, yet were very segmentalised. Dinsdale Landen was offered and accepted the role of Doctor Judson. Alfie Lynch, Nicholas Parsons and Annie Reid all wanted to do it . . . it was gonna be a great movie! Then the deputation arrived.

Nicholas Parsons as the doubtful Mr Wainwright. Will his faith betray him as the Haemovores attack? Photo © Tomek Bork.

Ian and Nicholas came to tell me they had found a camp in Crowborough, which they thought would be ideal. Most of it was unoccupied and they wanted me to join the camera recce (reconnaissance visit to locations with crew) the following week. Time was running out. Ian would spend the remainder of the pre-recce time seeking out the other locations. However their main reason for calling was to suggest that the ENTIRE production be shot on location, interiors and all!

The knicker-elastic money was wearing thin! The main concern June and myself had was the effect this idea would have on the design budget. Unless great care was taken, design furniture and furnishings, dressings etc, etc, would be hired for three weeks instead of the one week required for the studio. David Lasky, the designer, started doing sums again. For two days June and I thrashed through the implications. Were the man hours (hours required to build and paint scenery etc) available earlier than we'd booked them? Could the servicing departments off-load our design staff, as they might now finish this *Doctor Who* story two weeks earlier than we'd allowed? Will we get the money back if they can't? Will the artistes contracts work out cheaper as we require them for less time? And so on. Eventually all our questions were answered, and after weighing up the pros and cons, we agreed.

Nicholas was delighted. Ian was delighted but couldn't find a church with a flat roof! Our press office released our dilemma through Kent and Sussex papers, but a local historian came to the rescue first. Hawkhurst Church was perfect.

NEW LOCATIONS

Well, we had a splendid cast and crew, excellent locations for a terrific script . . . the O.B. recce would go like clockwork! I thought the camp looked very impressive, almost stuck in a time-warp; the cottage was good, the church was perfect, though we had to tarpaulin the flat roof. It was all going so well, I left the team to return to London, while the rest moved to Hastings,

the nearest beach. I knew that beach well. I'd walked along it many times with Mark Strickson (Turlough) and his wife, before they emigrated to Australia. Hastings had been their home and I'd visited them often. It was rocky, unspoiled and ideal. No it wasn't! The underwater camera would never be of any use there as the waters were too murky. "There's only one beach clear enough for underwater sequences like those required and it's at Lulworth Cove, Dorset, John" announced Paul, the cameraman the following day.

June and I put our heads together again. Dorset meant more hours to add to our shoot in order to travel there from Kent. I asked June where our Finance Assistant, Paul ►

The Parish Church of St. Laurence, Hawkhurst: centrepiece for the action in *The Curse of Fenric*.

Lovely weather for ducks! Recording *The Curse of Fenric* met with very changeable weather conditions, with scenery sinking into mud left by thawing snow . . . Photo © Gary Sigris.

Goodliffe, was hiding. "He's going through the budget with a fine tooth comb searching for anything spare. The knicker elastic's gone 'ping'." she replied.

We did find a little more spare cash, but there was now nothing left for emergencies – no over-runs, no last-minute requests, no nothing! Dee Baron, the make-up designer, had a problem, though. Dinsdale Landen had never worn contact lenses before. He'd had his lenses fitted and he could cope brilliantly, *but* he couldn't bear to put them in himself. "Can you pay for an optician to be on set whenever the lenses are needed?" Dee asked. What I wanted to say is unprintable, but artists' safety is paramount and the eyes are highly delicate organs of the body. "Yes, of course," I replied sweetly. "I'll ask Ian to schedule the 'lens' scenes as precisely, time-wise, as possible."

Shortly before the read-through I discussed the title again with Andrew Cartmel. I felt that the mention of 'Wolves' in the script came so late on in the story, that perhaps it wasn't as useful a title as we'd thought. Briggs to the rescue . . . and 'Wolves' became 'Curse', though much of the show's documentation showed 'Wolves' as the title.

The week's rehearsal went by so quickly! The Producer's run-through was combined with the Technical rehearsal and I was, apart from a few small points, delighted. Now all we had to do, was shoot it!

The design team spent several days prior to the shoot preparing Crowborough Army Camp for our requirements; dressing the interior of the barracks, dressing the exterior of the camp area and building the exterior of the tunnel and the entrance to the underground laboratory and store. The weather prior to and during the shoot was abysmal; rain, sleet, snow, hail,

storms were in abundance, and by the time we arrived to shoot, the two specially-built external structures had started to sink. However, we ploughed on, working through the worst weather I have ever experienced on location of any production in my career. One morning we arrived to discover the camp covered in snow; fortunately we were working mainly inside (Millington's office) but our excellent visual effects team used water hoses to clear the snow, wherever visible through the windows of the hut.

As if we didn't have enough to do already, I had agreed previously that a team from BBC Children's department could visit us on location, to record the disintegration of characters Jean and Phyllis. Time was short and we ended up rushing the sequence at the end of the day . . . the Children's show had its material but the director and I decided we should try and reshoot the effect on a piece of grass near the church location later on in the shoot.

By the time we came to shoot the 'designed' external structures, they had sunk some eighteen inches into the mud . . . the working conditions were dreadful. If you look closely at the sequences shot, you will doubtless note that the relationship of the artists to the structures is not quite to scale . . . eighteen inches not quite to scale! Also filmed at the barracks in a huge hangar was the massive James-Bond-like laboratory and store . . . known affectionately as Samantha Fox's bedroom!

From this location we moved to the church at Hawkhurst . . . many complex sequences were filmed here and we ended up having to stay for an extra half day. Even so, we were still behind schedule, so I shot sequences of Haemovores emerging from behind the tombstones and the re-shoot of the demise of Jean and Phyllis, on the Director's behalf.

PRESS CALLS

Miss Hardaker's cottage was relatively straightforward and the underground tunnels (in fact, the cellar of a local school), went by without a hiccup. However our last location, a disused British Railways tunnel was waterlogged and awash with mud. At one point forty of us were submerged into complete darkness in the tunnel due to a power failure. Sylvester McCoy's wife and sons had come to visit us on this particular day, and as they

Recording scenes for the final minutes of *The Curse of Fenric* in 'The Samantha Fox' bedroom. Photo © Steve Cook.

appeared a little bored, because Sylv was always busy, they were inserted into spare mini-versions of the heamovore costumes and used in the show. (See Part Four).

Joanne Kenny as one of the Haemovores. Photo © Tomek Bork.

I should add, at this point, that, almost every day, we were joined by members of the press; local press, nationals, **Doctor Who Magazine** who organised a Dalek photo shoot with Sylvester, SF magazines, we even did interviews for the NAAFI Times. We also had a visit from the Mayor of Brighton, whose sole objective was to be photographed with The Doctor! All this meant that Sylvester and Sophie Aldred, when they were not 'on set', were being interviewed or photographed throughout the shoot. BBC and BBC Enterprises photographers were on hand for several days to add to their work-load.

During this major first section of the shoot, the members of the unit stayed in hotels in and around Tunbridge Wells. I was delighted that I had been housed in an hotel directly opposite the theatre where I had written and directed a pantomime several years previously, starring Peter Davison, Anthony Ainley, Sandra Dickinson and The Wilson Sisters, who appeared briefly in *Delta and the Bannermen*. Despite the fact that everyone works extremely hard and long on location, evenings do tend to be the time for artists and staff to let their hair down. This shoot was no exception but people did tend to emerge from their rooms for the evening later than usual, due to the time it took to defrost!

After a day off we travelled to Dorset. The weather here was a little better but there were still regular showers and a biting wind.

The day we were using boats supplied by the Marines, they arrived late. When they did finally arrive, we had moved to another location. So we de-camped again to shoot the opening sequences of the story. Due to ever-changing winds, the visfx fog was extremely difficult to achieve. These delays and the boats' and dinghies' late appearance

At the end of Part Three, camp hut windows explode as Fenric takes control of Doctor Judson. Photo © Gary Sigris.

set us substantially behind schedule again, so far behind that we feared we couldn't recover.

So, it was decided that I would shoot the underwater sequences (a slow and painstaking process) on Nicholas' behalf whilst he shot other important sequences on the shore. Hopefully this would get us back on course.

The underwater sequences and others in the script involved artists, including Jean, Phyllis and Ace, immersed in the freezing water. Obviously shots were lined up as far as possible by using stand-ins in wetsuits, but I must say that the ladies (who had to stay in the water longest) displayed a totally professional attitude towards the job at hand, which was horrendous.

On our last day we were back on schedule and the final sequence that was shot was, in fact, the final sequence of the story . . . unusual in our business. It was a wrap!

On the first examination of the timed sequences, it appeared that there *might* have been sufficient material for a fifth episode. The ➤

Setting up an attack on the church. Haemovores rise from the cold waters of the English Channel. Photo © Sue Moore.

A Haemovore mask in an early stage of preparation. Photo © Sue Moore.

some of the material had to be junked.

With the addition of Mark Ayre's brilliantly haunting music and Dick Mills' special sound and the expertise of our Sound Supervisors, *The Curse of Fenric* was finally complete. But that isn't the end of the story.

A few months later, I was approached by BBC Home Video department with a view to re-instating some of the junked 'Fenric' material as a collectors item for the video market. I thought it an excellent idea and so did all concerned. I hope you did too.

So many people contributed to the making of this show; the costume assistant who, in order to operate the Ancient One's gills spent hours lying on a cold floor and a freezing seabed furthermore, without a murmur, the Haemovore extras, who became so unrecognisable that we had to re-name them (and they answered to their names): Popeye, Claire Rayner, Mrs Bridges, Demis Roussos, Mary Quant etc etc. (Quite why two of them were called 'The Grace Brothers' is still beyond me), the lady who ran the NAAFI who opened early when everyone was stiff with frost, providing she could have her photo taken with a Dalek, the Marines, the Stunt performers, the diving school, the fishermen, the hotelliers, the night watchman . . . all of them were part and parcel of the making of *Doctor Who*. To all of them and the entire cast and crew of *Fenric* my thanks. It was an ambitious project, yet we managed more than one hundred minutes of cut material (the average length of a feature film) in less than two weeks!

◄ correct procedure if this is on the cards, is to discuss with those directly concerned, namely writer, director and editor, whether it would be feasible to cut the story into five and discuss, armed with more detailed timings, where the episode endings would occur. If all of us were agreed of the soundness and integrity of the idea, the Controller of BBC1 would be contacted via the Head of Drama Series to see if he'd like a fifth episode. If he did, he would have to supply the additional money for payments to artists, writer, musicians etc.

Contrary to rumour, this was never really a viable proposition. The minute Nicholas started viewing the shot material, he realised that there had been a major timing error. All the episodes were, in fact, over long, but the total was nowhere near twenty-five minutes.

It was whilst viewing the material that it was discovered that some of our material had been wiped. This was material shot on a second camera, simultaneously recorded during the morning of the 'Samantha Fox bedroom' sequences. Consequently, the final scene between the Doctor, Ace, Sorin and the Ancient One is not precisely as Nicholas had planned, but with his judicious editing, we were both relatively happy not to attempt to reshoot, which would have been prohibitive. Furthermore this inadvertant wiping did not affect the timing of the episode.

After many days of viewing cassettes of his material, Nicholas

started to edit. As each episode was completed, it was viewed by myself and Nicholas and we discussed how to bring each programme down to time and the ways in which it might be improved.

Part Four was a major problem. It was way over length. Nicholas, Andrew and I had to re-structure the episode (cutting scenes in half, repositioning others, cutting others) in order to tell the story and make it fit our time-slot. Ian Briggs, the writer, liked what we did though was obviously sad, like all of us, that

Tea break for the heamovores. Photo © Mark Wyman.

First Call

Actress Sophie Aldred, who played the Doctor's companion, Ace, recalls the recording of *The Curse of Fenric*. . .

"Sophie!" Bang bang bang. "Sophie . . it's 6:30!" The voice of Judy Corrie, *Fenric*'s assistant floor manager, wends its way into a lovely dream I'm having about normal things like shopping in Tesco's and drinking cups of tea with friends in my kitchen. Oh *no!* Why did I stay up half the night in an armchair in the bar showing off with Tomek, Sylvester and the two Jo's, talking about changing the world and being screamingly funny – or so we thought at the time. If Sylv was a real Time Lord then he could have the decency to alter the morning call times, or at least do a bit of a fiddle with the alarm clocks so I could have my eight hours beauty sleep. And I could do with *that* at the moment.

Peering through half closed eyes into the cracked hotel mirror I thank goodness for make up and console myself that having given up alcohol two years ago, I will be feeling marginally better than some of my fellow actors this morning. Pulling on some track suit trousers, vest, two t-shirts, two jumpers and my thick ski jacket, I stumble down to reception and greet the crew members on an early recording call.

Hardly a word is spoken as we board the coach and drive from Tunbridge Wells town centre to Crowborough Training Camp, where the army bits from *The Curse of Fenric* are being shot. I try not to blame myself too hard for having come up with the brilliant idea, all those months ago in John Nathan-Turner's nice warm office in Shepherd's Bush, of having a Forties hair do, make up and costumier so that Ace wouldn't look too out of place when she stepped out of the TARDIS. Little did I realise that it would take over an hour to prepare for this, sitting in a freezing army hut, huddled in blankets, nursing hot cups of tea.

Poor Dee (Baron) valiantly wrestles with two hair extensions and my "sprouts", as we called my rolls of hair carefully placed in a red string snood that her Mum had crotcheted for the occasion. Mind you, by the time we'd finished all the gossip and more putting the world to rights (actors seem to spend a lot of time doing that but, like those chatty cab drivers you get, never seem to be able to get round to *doing* anything about it) my sprouts were in place.

Sara, my dresser, had done me proud with thermal vests and knickers and a thick coat in which I could rehearse right up until a take. Even so, it's *cold* today and wet and horrible, and most of the scenes are going to be outside. So fortified with my daily black pudding and tomato bun, I venture out into the mud, with a sleepy looking Sylvester, who has sneakily managed to incorporate a duffle coat into his characterisation of the Doctor in this particular story.

EXPLOSIVE WORK

I won't bore you with the camera set ups, the scenes, the incredibly long time it takes to shoot a couple of minutes on two camera, first a wide angle, then close ups, and then other angles for good measure. The bits I like are of course the explosions, and Sylv and I had a brilliant one this morning where the visual effects crew had to blow up a hut behind us as we ran from the doorway. Stunt co-ordinator Tip Tipping was on hand to help Sylv and me look as daredevil as possible – he knows we like to compete for who can jump highest, dive furthest, look the most death defying – and he shows us how to land safely as we jump over a heap of sandbags into a pile of wet cold muck. A couple of rehearsals for cameras and timing and then we're off! There's ➤

something about stunts that makes your heart beat faster and wish you hadn't had that extra cup of tea for elevenses.

Nick Mallet wants us to hold hands while we run, and I tell him how annoyed I get when namby pamby tv characters run along holding each other back by clinging on to each other – how can you possibly run fast and look cool with some bloke dragging along beside you. Sylv tells me off for being bossy. Ian Fraser, the production manager, tells us to be quiet and stand by. Inside the hut the charges are all set and we just hope they all go off in this wet drizzle. I'm hoping I don't fall flat on my face in the inches of thick mud between the doorway and the sandbags.

Ian's hand drops and we run, reaching the sandbags and jumping just as an enormous explosion rips the air behind us, and debris raining down on us both. "Cut!"

"Hmm, that was a good one, eh Soph?" says Sylv rhetorically.

Soon after that we break for lunch and trudge up to the top of the camp where the culinary expertise of Mange Tout, the location caterers, has been tested to the full in rising winds and freezing rain. It never ceases to amaze me how three people in a little van can produce the kind of menu you'd be hard pushed to equal in a Soho restaurant. I always go for the buffet: asparagus, scampi, salads of all kinds, even squid, escargots, and, one day, frogs legs, which I'm glad to say went untouched. Working with Jo on *Corners* has made me a little squeamish about actually eating little green things!

I sit with Tomek Bork, Marek Anton and Marcus Hutton, who are all looking very dashing in their uniforms and who are tucking into huge plates of steak, curry, or vegetable lasagne. "No wonder you get cold, Sophie!" shouts Tomek. "You eat nothing – eat, eat!"

"I am eating, Tomek."

"Ah, you English women – you should have Polish food. *That* would make you warm!" I resist the temptation to wolf down a bowl of roly poly pudding, or Banoffee pie, Mange Tout's speciality. My tailored suit is already beginning to show signs of strains round the waistband after a few days of "eating to keep warm".

After several cups of coffee (which I later regret, having to visit the one makeshift army toilet to struggle with my thermal knickers and suspender belt in the freezing cold) we slip and slide down to the next location on the agenda, to shoot some indoor scenes, thank goodness. We run quite smoothly through my bits with Sylv in the bunk room and move into the larger dormitory, and it's here that I have

Antics at Crowborough Army Camp! Photo © Tomek Bork.

my strange experience of suddenly realising that I'm involved in making the programme which scared me so much as a child.

Cory Pulman (playing my Grandmother), Aaron, the baby playing my mother (his first role in drag at six months, as JN-T pointed out) and I huddle together on the floor pretending to shelter from an unknown force outside. Nick had told us that the Haemovores would appear at the window, but what actually happens as we're waiting for something a bit naff to occur is a sudden smashing of the windows, a gust of wind and strange misshapen faces leering at us while weird hands grope through the sugar glass. For a split second it all seems very real: Cory screams and grips my arm and the baby starts crying. Ace takes over from Sophie, snatches the baby and rushes to the window – but that one moment remains to haunt me in dreams.

VISUALLY AFFECTED

Back outside, it's stopped raining but for continuity the visual effects crew have to haul out the sprinklers and cover us all in wet cold hose water for the rest of the day. I have a sticky moment as Cory hands me the baby, and I run towards the car in which she and my "Mother" escape to form Ace's future: my shoes stick in the morass of mud, I

start to slip and just manage to regain my balance and hold onto poor Aaron, who, like the true pro that he is, remains fast asleep. I take a sneaky look over at his Mum who, luckily, is engaged in conversation with one of the make up team. I'm sure if she'd realised the ordeals Aaron would have to face, she may not have been so keen to offer his services. I just hope he's not haunted by Haemovores as he grows up! It'll be strange for him to show his children that video!

The only time he becomes slightly peturbed is when we arrive at the car and the cold sprinkler water hits him full in the face; he wakes up and starts crying, which turns out to be perfect for the scene. I'm so wet and cold and my hair, which is completely full of spray, has gone completely solid and I'm shivering like a drowned rat, so Sarah piles warm coats on me. Tomek, my official "bodywarmer" gives me a hug under his army greatcoat, and Dee rushes me off to the make up hut for a quick zizz with the hairdryer. Then it's on with the scene.

This time, here's one of those *Doctor Who* moments of imagining something that's not really there and will be edited in later. Ace is meant to be watching Jean and Phyllis whither away, something which the two Jo's obviously cannot do, being very much flesh and blood, albeit long nailed, white faced and freezing cold! Nick directs me brilliantly: as sound is not needed he talks me through the reactions, showing me the eyeline with his hand, and describing quietly and eloquently the imaginary scene before me. I'm quite moved, and we break for tea.

There's such a lot of waiting involved in any kind of filming, as anyone who's visited locations will confirm, and then when it's time for your scene, there never seems to be enough time to shoot it properly. Luckily there are always wonderful casts and crews who alleviate any boredom on *Doctor Who* who more than make up for the waiting, the cold, the uncomfortable costumes and the lumpy hotel beds! *The Curse of Fenric* was no exception and there are wonderful moments to remember: Nicholas Parsons' amazing ability to nod off any place, anytime, Dinsdale Landen's mischievous twinkling eyes which made me burst out laughing in close ups; and Alfie Lynch trying to get his tongue round the mythical incantations and technical jargon invented for him by Ian Briggs.

And those magic words "It's a wrap" which means wearily climbing out of that muddy clammy suit and the soaking thermals which Sarah will have to wash and dry before tomorrow. How comfortable and warm my track suit trousers and jumpers feel, how nice it is to scrape off that caked on make up and mud, and that bath back at the hotel, and the meal in a superb Chinese restaurant which we discover and the confortable talk about the day's work followed by . . . putting the world to rights pushes away evil thoughts of that alarm clock set to 6:30 tomorrow morning. Night, night.

THE CURSE OF FENRIC (7M)

The Doctor and his companion, Ace, arrive at an army camp in 1943. As the Second World War rages, strange things are happening in this North Yorkshire town and even stranger forces are gathering; Russian commandos preparing to attack the base are attacked in the night and the British commander, Millington, seems obsessed with "The Wolves of Fenric". In the local church the computer scientist Doctor Judson seeks to decipher some Viking inscriptions whilst the local vicar, Mr Wainwright, has misgivings about the war itself.

As events progress, the Doctor and Ace uncover the threat of the Haemovores and Millington's plot against Britain's wartime ally, the Soviet Union. Meanwhile, Ace is drawn to Kathleen Dudman and her young baby, not knowing why. The Doctor knows what is happening and soon he is once again pitted against Fenric, a malevolent evil force who has engineered events to escape a trap set by the Doctor in the past. Ace is a pawn in a deadly game and as the Haemovores attack British and Russian soldiers alike, as friends and enemies fall before Fenric's plan, the Doctor himself faces one of his most dangerous threats. . .

CAST

Sylvester McCoy *(The Doctor)*, Sophie Aldred *(Ace)*, Dinsdale Landen *(Doctor Judson)*, Alfred Lynch *(Commander Millington)*, Tomek Bork *(Captain Sorin)*, Nicholas Parsons *(The Rev Mr Wainwright)*, Joanne Kenny *(Jean)*, Joanne Bell *(Phyllis)*, Peter Czajkowski *(Sgt Prozorov)*, Cory Pulman *(Kathleen Dudman)*, Aaron Hanley *(Baby)*, Marek Anton *(Vershinin)*, Steven Rimkus *(Capt. Bates)*, Marcus Hutton *(Sgt. Leigh)*, Janet Henfrey *(Miss Hardaker)*, Anne Reid *(Nurse Crane)*, Mark Conrad *(Petrossian)*, Christien Anholt *(Perkins)*, Raymond Trickett *(Ancient Haemovore)*, Cy Town, Ian Elliott *(Haemovores)*.

CREDITS

Written by Ian Briggs. Stunt Arranger: Tip Tipping. Visual Effects Designer: Graham Brown. Costume Designer: Ken Trew. Incidental Music: Mark Ayres. Title Music by Ron Grainer, arranged by Keff McCulloch. Script Editor: Andrew Cartmel. Designer: David Laskey. Producer: John Nathan-Turner. Director: Nicholas Mallett.

BROADCAST DETAILS

Part One	25th October 1989	7.35pm – 8.00pm
Part Two	1st November 1989	7.35pm – 8.00pm
Part Three	8th November 1989	7.35pm – 8.00pm
Part Four	15th November 1989	7.35pm – 8.00pm

BARB Viewing Figures (in Millions): 4.3, 4.0, 4.0, 4.2
Audience Appreciation Figures: 67%, 68%, 68%, 68%.
Target Books Novelisation: The Curse of Fenric by Ian Briggs
BBC Video Catalogue Number: BBCV 4453